SACRED EARTH DRAMAS

Sponsored by
the World Wide Fund
for Nature, UK
and
The Arts for Nature

SACRED EARTH DRAMAS

An anthology of winning plays from the 1990 competition of the Sacred Earth Drama Trust

faber and faber
LONDON · BOSTON

First published in Great Britain in 1993
by Faber and Faber Limited
3 Queen Square London WC1N 3AU

Photoset by Parker Typesetting Service, Leicester
Printed in Great Britain by Clays Ltd, St Ives plc

A CIP record for this book
is available from the British Library

ISBN 0 571 16290 8

2 4 6 8 10 9 7 5 3 1

Contents

FOREWORD
by Ted Hughes vii

INTRODUCTION
by Toni Arthur ix

GIFTS OF FLAME
by David Calcutt, England 1
First prize: 15 and over

BUFFALO DANCE
by Class 5 (1990), Ecole Internationale de Genève, Switzerland 37
First prize: under 15

CHIPKO, Bread and Puppet Theatre
by Ecole d'Humanité, Switzerland 63
Joint second prize: 15 and over

THE TALE OF MIGHTY HAWK AND MAGIC FISH
by Jo Dorras and Peter Walker for Wan Smolbag Theatre, Vanuatu 75
Joint second prize: 15 and over

NATURE'S REVENGE
by Bhupesh Malhotra, Finland 109
Second prize: under 15

CHILDREN OF THE RAINBOW
by André Surridge, New Zealand 123
Third prize: 15 and over

GREENHEART AND THE DRAGON POLLUTANT
by Cressida Miles, England 137
Highly commended: 15 and over

THINK GLOBAL, ACT LOCO
by Rick Whisenand, Thailand 149
Highly commended: 15 and over

PERSEPHONE AND THE RUBBISH BIN
by St Peter's Youth Group, Scotland 165
Highly commended: 15 and over

SACRED EARTH DRAMA COMPETITION:
TERMS AND CONDITIONS 179

Foreword

We have no problem in becoming aware that we are destroying our planet and our life on it. Our problem is the very great difficulty of becoming aware in such a way that we do something about it.

HRH The Duke of Edinburgh made the point: no knowledge can change the way we live unless it reaches the heart and soul and changes us there. But this is 'the very great difficulty'. How do you get a new piece of knowledge to the heart and soul of a human being?

It turns out to be almost impossible. Our incredible quickness in saying 'Yes, I understand perfectly', or 'But you are ignoring certain problems . . .', and our incredibly well-developed methods of flashing information instantly round the Earth, as if that were all we needed to do with it, serve one purpose only: they defend our hearts and souls from any piece of new knowledge. So that we can carry on as we were, with a good conscience.

The Duke of Edinburgh had the idea that the new knowledge needs to be couched in language that bypasses verbal argument – language that comes from the heart and soul and therefore speaks directly to the heart and soul. In 1986 he organized a conference of the heads of religions from all over the world, at Assisi, to consider how a new environmental awareness might be incorporated into religious teachings. After that, he asked whether the various languages of art could convey the same new awareness. Arts For Nature was founded as a response to Prince Philip's question. At the same time, in the same way, as an experiment, the Sacred Earth Drama Trust came into being.

By 'Sacred Earth Drama' we meant plays for people of all ages, based on environmental themes, to be used in schools and other places of learning, where they would provide an opportunity for young people to become fully involved in the issues – all the better if they could be performed by the young people themselves. From experience, we knew that young people's drama can be imaginative, inventive, yet at the same time simple and moving, to a degree that adult drama rarely can. Also from experience, we knew that adults, parents and teachers watch children's drama through the eyes of the child within themselves. It reaches them in ways they never can be reached if addressed simply as adults.

There is an extra pathos and truth when the young participate in plays which face the problems they inherit from us. We older generations are cashing in the world so fast and freely because we do not yet have to pay. If we do not pay the bill now, those coming after us certainly must. We all know that, when the bill falls due, the poorer ones who cannot pay in cash, with efforts that we hardly dare to contemplate, will pay with their lives. Everywhere, the poisoned and starving landscapes are beginning to show up. And those who will be forced to pay that bill, in full, in the future, are the very same young people who are performing in these plays now. Therefore the special pathos and truth. And therefore, maybe, a special power to awaken us to what we are doing, and to change our lives and theirs before it is too late.

We held a competition, advertising it in countries around the world, for short, imaginative plays for people of all ages, based on environmental themes, using mythic or traditional stories. From the many we received, our judges chose the nine selected here. This collection is only a first step. The next is to distribute it in other countries translated into other languages.

Our hope is to supply schools with this powerful means of involving young people and their communities in these issues. And we also hope that the examples here will encourage teachers and acting groups, or indeed anybody, to invent similar plays, not necessarily in the same style but with a similar purpose.

Ted Hughes

Introduction

This anthology of nine plays is the end result of a worldwide play-writing competition inaugurated by the Sacred Earth Drama Trust in 1990. The playwrights were invited to submit plays that updated, reshaped and retold an existing religious or mythological story with particular relevance to the natural world today, and how we should live in it. The response was overwhelming. Packages of all shapes and sizes arrived from places as disparate as Africa, America, India, New Zealand, Australia, Thailand, Vanuatu, Finland and Britain. Some of the plays were presented in video or cassette form. Some were professionally printed, using the latest in desk-top-publishing techniques. Some were handwritten on rice paper. What they all had in common was a desperate cry from the heart to save what is left of our planet. The plays were emotive, exciting and, above all, effective. Each demonstrated a need to listen to the voices of our ancestors and heed their ancient warnings. That their messages were considered for so long to be archaic and of little relevance to our modern world is to our detriment.

Practically without exception the themes were culled from traditional stories that were created to help establish cultural identities and cultural cohesion within the many differing communities. Originally these stories were passed down from one age to the next by word of mouth – an oral tradition which was considered an essential method of communication between the young and old. Sitting at the feet of their acknowledged wiser elders, the rising generation would have the mysteries of life explained to them. The stories would be regularly repeated so that in time, when the young became the elders, they, too, could pass them on. The origins of the universe, the beginning of the human race and the secrets of the seasons were the first tales told. As each culture faced changes in their living conditions more stories were added to their oral history. Each one was shaped by the community to adjust and restructure their standards of morality, enabling them to live in peace and harmony within their own particular environment.

It was the advent of the written word that suppressed these all too necessary adjustments. Once a story was written down it became sacrosanct. Although the writing permanently preserved the tales and made them accessible for all posterity, in many ways the process hindered further development of the stories. They could no longer move with changing situations. Some, especially those of the Western world, became ignored and eventually forgotten. The wisdom of the elders was banished, considered inferior to modern technologies and regarded as outmoded superstition. Avarice was fed by these technologies with no respect to the consequences. What was taken from the Earth started to be considered a right, not an honour, and the use, or misuse, of the planet and its inhabitants carried no thought of a divine retribution.

Fortunately not all civilizations rejected their traditional ways. Many peoples still revere their ancestral heritage. The Aborigines of Australia, with their culture rooted in the land, have had, out of necessity, to work and live much of their time within the structure of a culture not their own. To help their people adjust to the outside influences which they were not traditionally equipped to conquer, they have created new stories. Their tales now tell of the management of racial conflict, social disease and psychological stress, all of which keep the traditional standards of morality within their culture and help to place the individual within the changed structure of their world. They have no desire to have the many thousands of years of their cultural development swallowed up by being part of an amorphous global village. To think and act globally it is not necessary to lose personal identity. All the first stories ever told, within whatever culture, addressed the mystery of being and how to continue that being. The tales manifested themselves individually to each different society, but the central aims were the same – to live in peace and harmony with nature. Somewhere along the progressive journey of life many seem to have lost the awe that was felt in being and seem to have also lost the care needed to continue to be.

Yet the equipment is still there, even in the most sceptical. Whispered in corridors, classrooms and conference centres, even the most sophisticated tell cautionary tales. These are the contemporary legends, the 'friend of a friend' tales. All over the world these tales, true apologues, warn of drinking untested water, giving lifts to strangers or rejoicing in an unfair bargain. The list of the subject matters is endless. Most people know them, most people tell them and most people have been forewarned by them. If stories such as these rule the consciences of our everyday lives, then why have we ignored the stories that govern our very existence?

The Kogi people from Colombia – a totally oral community – are so personally affected by the irresponsible damage to the planet that they have ventured, away from their self-imposed isolation, to try and remind us – the younger brothers – of these stories. These are people that most 'sophisticated' nations would term primitive. They have looked at the global results of this blinkered search for 'prosperity at all costs' and decided that the wisdom of the 'elder brothers' must be conveyed. They offer, in the guise of the powerful parables of their own culture, solutions to the plight of the Earth: solutions which require the return to the principles of give and take, reap and sow; solutions that would mean economic upheaval and individual denial. Is there the strength and ability to heed their message?

From the results of this play-writing competition it is obvious there is a will to stop the offences against nature. Having used the device of dramatizing and updating the old tales, the writers do not erect political platforms from which to speak, they use no subversive techniques, they simply and conscientiously 'tell it as it should be'. They bring to life the art of the old storyteller and speak directly to all of us, from whatever culture.

The Sacred Earth Drama Trust had originally thought that these plays should be for the enlightenment of young people and be performed only by them. What has become apparent during their reading is an underlying message within them all. These are not plays simply for one age category, they are for each and every one of us. Whatever group, school or institution decides to perform them, all within that community should join together to portray and to receive them. All the plays reach down to us from the mists of time and from our collective ancestral heritage.

If we act together we can save the world.

Toni Arthur

FIRST PRIZE: 15 AND OVER

GIFTS OF FLAME

by David Calcutt

WALSALL, WEST MIDLANDS, ENGLAND

Characters

STORYTELLER
BOY
GRANDMOTHER
ROCK
SUME
JURUPARI
MOTHER
GUIOMAR
SHAMAN
OLD WOMAN
MONAN
INKARI
GIANT TOAD
CHIEF
JAGUAR
1ST VILLAGER
2ND VILLAGER
3RD VILLAGER
4TH VILLAGER

Note: In circumstances where there may only be a small group of actors, it will be possible for some of the actors to play more than one character.

The STORYTELLER *enters and speaks to the audience.*

STORYTELLER: Once, long ago, in the early days of the world, before stories had ever come into the world, there was a boy who lived with his grandmother.

(*The* BOY *and the* GRANDMOTHER *enter. The* GRANDMOTHER *carries a bow and some arrows.*)

The boy's mother and father were dead, and he only had his grandmother to care for him in all the world, and she only had him. One day, the grandmother said to the boy –

GRANDMOTHER: You must go into the forest to get food. If you don't hunt, we'll starve.

STORYTELLER: And she gave the boy the bow and arrows that had belonged to his father.

GRANDMOTHER: With this bow, your father killed many animals when he was alive. With these arrows he killed many enemies. With this bow and these arrows, your father became a great hunter and warrior.

(*The* BOY *takes the bow and arrows.*)

BOY: The boy took the bow and arrows. He felt his father's strength in them. The strength flowed into his own arms. Now, he hoped, he would become a great hunter and warrior as well.

STORYTELLER: So the boy said goodbye to his grandmother, and went off into the forest to hunt. And she watched him go, walking through the trees, until she couldn't see him any more.

GRANDMOTHER: She watched him until he had disappeared into the darkness of the forest, and she didn't know that she would never see him in this world again.

(GRANDMOTHER *goes. The* BOY *hunts stealthily through the forest as the* STORYTELLER *speaks.*)

STORYTELLER: The boy went into the forest. Deeper and deeper he went. He had never been so deep in the forest before.

BOY: It was dark. Shadows moved. He heard noises and voices. He was afraid.

STORYTELLER: There were demons in the forest. Terrible demons, like Curupir, who walks with his feet facing backwards.

BOY: Timakana, who wears human heads round his neck.

STORYTELLER: Jurupari, who sucks the breath from your body.

BOY: Demons that drink your blood and leave your skin hanging empty.

STORYTELLER: That bite off your head and spit out the bones.

BOY: That creep up on you and snatch you away –

STORYTELLER: – and nobody ever sees you again!

BOY: No!

(*The* BOY *cries out in fear and hides his face. Pause.*)

STORYTELLER: But at last, the boy came to the very centre of the forest. And there, standing before him, between two trees, he saw –

(*The* BOY *raises his head.*)

BOY: A deer!

(*The* STORYTELLER *now stands before the* BOY *as the Deer.*)

STORYTELLER: The boy rose to his feet. He looked in wonder at the deer.

BOY: The deer looked at the boy. It didn't move.

STORYTELLER: Slowly, the boy took out an arrow.

BOY: Still the deer didn't move.

STORYTELLER: And even as he fitted the arrow to the string of his bow –

BOY: It didn't seem afraid, it just went on looking at him –

STORYTELLER: Even as he drew back the string of his bow –

BOY: It just went on standing there, watching him –

STORYTELLER: Even as he raised his bow and took aim –

BOY: The deer stood there calmly, looking straight into his eyes –

STORYTELLER: As if it knew the arrow would never be loosed –

BOY: And, as the boy was about to loose the arrow and kill the deer –

STORYTELLER: A voice spoke.

ROCK: Leave that deer!

(The BOY *stops in surprise and fear. He looks round. The* STORYTELLER *stops being the Deer now.)*

STORYTELLER: The boy looked round. Who had spoken? He couldn't see anybody. The voice spoke again.

ROCK: Leave that deer alone! Don't kill it!

STORYTELLER: He looked into the shadows. Was someone there? Was it a demon?

BOY: Who's speaking? What are you?

STORYTELLER: He shivered in fear. Perhaps it was a demon that was speaking to him. Once more, the voice spoke.

ROCK: Don't kill that deer. Put down your bow and arrows.

BOY: Who is it? Where are you? I can't see you!

STORYTELLER: – said the boy. And the voice said –

ROCK: I'm here. Right in front of you.

BOY: Here?

ROCK: Yes.

BOY: Where?

ROCK: Here!

STORYTELLER: The boy looked, but all he could see was a large rock, rising up out of the earth.

ROCK: I'm here. You're looking at me.

(The BOY *approaches a large rock from which we and he now realize the voice is coming.)*

STORYTELLER: And then the boy realized that the voice was coming from inside the rock.

BOY: Here?

ROCK: At last.

STORYTELLER: The rock, or something that lived inside the rock, was speaking to him.

BOY: What do you want?

ROCK: I want you to let that deer live. I want you to give me your bow and arrows, and never hunt anything again.

BOY: But if I do that, me and my grandmother will have nothing to eat. If I don't hunt, we'll die.

ROCK: Do as I say, and I'll give you something more important than food. Something more important than fire, or water, or air. I'll give you something that's stronger than death, and will make you live for ever.

BOY: What's more important than all those things? What can make people live for ever?

ROCK: Stories.

STORYTELLER: – said the rock.

ROCK: I'll give you stories.

BOY: Stories?

STORYTELLER: – said the boy.

BOY: What are stories?

STORYTELLER: The boy didn't know what stories were. He'd never heard of them. In those days, there were no stories in the world.

BOY: I don't know what you're talking about.

STORYTELLER: So the rock told him.

ROCK: Stories are what you are. They are where you came from and how you were made. Stories are why things are as they are, and how they came to be. They are the whole world, and everything beyond the world, and it's time you knew what they were. Sit down on the ground, and I'll tell you all the stories there are, and then you'll know them.

(*The* BOY *sits beside the rock.*)

STORYTELLER: So the boy put down his bow and arrows. He sat on the ground, and he listened, as the rock began to tell him its stories. And what stories did the rock tell the boy? First of all it told –

ROCK: – the first story of all, of our mother the earth, and how she gave birth to everything that is on the earth, the forests and the mountains –

STORYTELLER: – the rivers and lakes –

ROCK: – the birds and insects and animals, everything that

lives and grows –
STORYTELLER: – everything that jumps and creeps –
ROCK: – and crawls and runs –
STORYTELLER: – and flies and wriggles and swims –
ROCK: – everything came out of her body at the beginning –
STORYTELLER: – and goes back to her body in the end.
ROCK: And finally, she gave birth to two children, Sume and Jurupari, twins who hated each other, and were born fighting.
(SUME *and* JURUPARI *enter, fighting, struggling, rolling, kicking, punching. They call out as they fight.*)
SUME: They tore up the forests!
JURUPARI: They ripped up the mountains!
SUME: They sucked up the seas and spat them out!
JURUPARI: They stamped great holes in the ground with their feet.
SUME: They bit –
JURUPARI: – and they kicked –
SUME: – and they clawed –
JURUPARI: – and they pawed!
ROCK: Each one trying to destroy the other. But they couldn't. So they just went on fighting, until –
(*Their* MOTHER *enters.*)
MOTHER: Stop it! Stop it, both of you! Look what you're doing! You're destroying everything!
(SUME *and* JURUPARI *ignore her and carry on fighting.*)
Stop it, I said!
(*She hits them both and pulls them apart.*)
Now! That's enough! No more! If I'd known you were going to cause all this trouble, I wouldn't have given birth to you. Which of you started it?
JURUPARI: It was him!
SUME: No, it wasn't, it was him!
JURUPARI: It wasn't me!
SUME: Yes, it was!
JURUPARI: You started it!

SUME: I didn't!

JURUPARI: You did!

(*They start to fight again.* MOTHER *hits them and pulls them apart.*)

MOTHER: No more, I said! You're both to blame! And you're also both my children. I want you to make friends, and promise never to fight each other again.

(SUME *and* JURUPARI *stare at each other sulkily.*)

Make friends. Shake hands.

SUME: All right. (SUME *holds out his hand to* JURUPARI.) No hard feelings?

JURUPARI: No hard feelings.

(JURUPARI *takes* SUME*'s hand. As he clasps it he drags* SUME *forward, hits him, and knocks him to the ground. Then he stamps on him. He gives a cry of triumph and turns to his* MOTHER.)

There! Now you've got only one son, and you can give all your love to me!

(MOTHER *stares at him in horror.*)

MOTHER: You'll get no love from me! For what you've just done I cast you out from my love for ever. You'll never know love again. Go from here! Run! Hide! Hide yourself in the darkest places of the earth. From this day forward you'll know only hatred and fear, and the pain for your crime will burn you for all time!

(JURUPARI *gives a cry of pain and anguish.*)

JURUPARI: Mother!

MOTHER: You are not my son!

(*Howling,* JURUPARI *runs off.* MOTHER *goes to* SUME *and kneels next to him.*)

ROCK: So Jurupari, the first murderer, ran and hid himself. His heart was filled with hatred and pain, with longing and loss. He became hideous to look at, a monster, dwelling always in the dark places of the earth –

STORYTELLER: – and he dwells there still, sending his hatred out into the world, infecting us with bad dreams and evil

thoughts. He lives in fear, and we live in fear of him.
BOY: Jurupari, the Father of all Demons.
ROCK: That's right.
BOY: But what about Sume? Did he really die?
ROCK: No. He couldn't die, because in those days Death hadn't come into the world. In those days, Life was so new and so strong, it was stronger than Death. But the blow Jurupari gave him felled him, and he couldn't wake up again. So his mother, the Earth, knelt beside him, and whispered in his ear.
MOTHER: Dream, my son. Dream, and let your dreams populate the world. Dream the world healing from the damage you've caused. Dream life returning, dream it walking on two legs and speaking.
BOY: Us? He dreamed us?
ROCK: Yes. He dreamed us hatching from a giant egg. And he's still dreaming us.
STORYTELLER: That's who we are. His dream.
ROCK: Everything that's happened since then, everything that's happening now, and will happen in the future, it's all part of his dream.
STORYTELLER: And, as long as he keeps dreaming, things will keep happening, and we'll keep on going.
BOY: But what will happen when he wakes?
ROCK: Don't worry about that. It's a long time off yet.
BOY: Are there any more stories?
ROCK: Of course. That was only the first. There are hundreds more, thousands. Enough to keep us going till tomorrow morning.
BOY: Tell me some more, then.
ROCK: All right. Listen.
STORYTELLER: So the rock continued to tell the boy its stories. It told him stories of the first people, and how they gave names to all the creatures –
ROCK: And how each creature got its colour.
STORYTELLER: Where the bat came from.

ROCK: How monkeys came to be, and why we must never take notice of them.
STORYTELLER: Why the snake is immortal.
ROCK: How women were given the sacred flutes.
STORYTELLER: And how Jurupari stole them from women and gave them to men.
ROCK: Why the Jaguar was made the Guardian of Fire.
STORYTELLER: And how Monan stole it and gave it to people.
BOY: Monan? Is that what you said?
ROCK: Yes. Monan.
BOY: Who's Monan?
ROCK: A great hero. Apart from stealing fire, he did many other marvellous things as well. It's his story I'm going to tell you now. Listen very carefully to it. It's possibly the most important story of all.
BOY: Why?
ROCK: Stop asking questions and just listen. Once there was a young woman named Guiomar who had just had a baby. She was very happy because it was her first baby. It was a boy, and she had called him Botoque.

(GUIOMAR *enters, carrying the baby, singing to it softly.*)

BOY: Is that her?
ROCK: Yes. She walks by the river with her child. She sings to him, and looks at him with love.
GUIOMAR: Botoque. My little son. How fierce your eyes are. And your cry. I've never heard such a cry. With such eyes and such a cry, when you grow, you will make the earth shake.

(*The* SHAMAN *enters speaking to* GUIOMAR *suddenly.*)

SHAMAN: What's that you're carrying?
GUIOMAR: What?
SHAMAN: There, in your arms.
BOY: Who's that?
ROCK: A shaman. A most powerful shaman. The spirits speak to him, and when he speaks all people listen.
SHAMAN: What is it?

GUIOMAR: It's my son. His name is Botoque.

SHAMAN: That isn't his name. I'll tell you what his real name is. It's death.

GUIOMAR: What do you mean?

SHAMAN: You carry death in your arms. If he lives, he will bring pain and suffering to all our people. I see people falling on the ground. I see their eyes roll white. Their bodies are cold. They do not move. Where they spoke there is silence, where they moved there is stillness. All this, through him.

GUIOMAR: It's not true!

SHAMAN: I speak only the truth! I speak what the spirits show me! They have shown me this. If we are to live, that child must die.

GUIOMAR: No!

SHAMAN: It must be done!

GUIOMAR: He's my son – I won't –

SHAMAN: The men of the village will come, they will take him –

GUIOMAR: They'll never take him!

SHAMAN: By your own hands, then. Give him to the river. Let the river take his death, (*Pause.*) You have no choice.

(SHAMAN *goes.*)

GUIOMAR: My little son. How can I do this? You look up at me with your fierce, bright eyes, and they're full of trust. Yet I am the one who must take your life! Why is the world so hard? It's too much for anyone to bear! (*She sits, cradling the Child.*)

ROCK: For a long time she sat, by the river, hugging her son to her. She felt the terrible weight of the earth beneath her feet. She felt the terrible weight of the sky above her head. The child slept peacefully in her arms and her body was filled with the heaviness of the world.

BOY: What did she do?

ROCK: She rose. She walked towards the river. The child

was still sleeping. Gently, tenderly, she lowered her child to the waters of the river.

(*As the* ROCK *has spoken,* GUIOMAR *has stood and walked a few paces towards the river. She now lowers the Child towards it. An* OLD WOMAN *enters, suddenly.*)

OLD WOMAN: Stop.

(GUIOMAR *turns.*)

OLD WOMAN: Give the child to me.

GUIOMAR: You?

OLD WOMAN: Yes. I'll take him far from here. I'll raise him as my own. He'll be my son. No one need know.

GUIOMAR: Who are you?

OLD WOMAN: Does it matter? I'm the one who will save your son's life, that's all you need to know. Give him to me.

GUIOMAR: Why do you want him?

OLD WOMAN: Again, that's my business. It doesn't concern you. Well?

GUIOMAR: I don't know . . .

OLD WOMAN: Give him to the river, then.

GUIOMAR: You'll take him far away?

OLD WOMAN: Yes.

GUIOMAR: I'll never see him again.

OLD WOMAN: But you'll know he's alive, somewhere in the world.

GUIOMAR: Yes. (*Pause.*) Take him! (*She gives the Child quickly to the* OLD WOMAN.) He's a good child.

OLD WOMAN: I can see that.

GUIOMAR: Look after him well.

OLD WOMAN: I will.

GUIOMAR: He has a loud cry –

OLD WOMAN: I know. I've heard him. (*Pause.*) You'd better go, now.

GUIOMAR: Yes.

(*She turns to go, then stops and turns back.*)

Let me have one last look at him –

OLD WOMAN: No! He's my child, now. To you, he's dead!

(GUIOMAR *turns sadly and goes. The* OLD WOMAN *speaks to the child.*)

Now, little son, we've got a long journey to go on, so we'd best get started. I'm an old woman, older than anybody knows, and I can't move so fast, these days. Who knows how long it will take us, eh? But that doesn't matter. We've got all the time we want, you and me. All the time in the world.

(*The* OLD WOMAN *takes the Child off.*)

BOY: So the child Botoque was saved from drowning, and became Death's son.

BOY: What did you say? Death's son? That old woman was Death?

ROCK: Yes, that's right. She was Death.

STORYTELLER: Death, who sings sweet songs to us, so sweet that we never want to stop listening to them, we don't want them to end. So we follow her, we leave our homes and our families, and our friends, we follow her across the world, out of the world, listening only to the sweetness and beauty of her songs, until we forget everything, we forget even who we are, and we're lost in her songs for ever.

BOY: Did she sing her songs to the baby?

ROCK: No. She wanted him to live, and be her son. She took him to the cave where she lived, on top of a high mountain on the other side of the world. And there she raised him, and taught him all the wonders and secrets of the world. And there, too, she gave him a new name.

STORYTELLER: Monan.

ROCK: Yes, Monan.

(MONAN *enters. He carries a spear. He is hunting, silently, looking, sniffing the ground, stopping. The* OLD WOMAN *enters.*)

OLD WOMAN: Monan –

(MONAN *raises a finger to his lips.*)

Monan, what are you –

MONAN: Quiet, mother. I'm hunting.
OLD WOMAN: Hunting? For what?
MONAN: A bird.
OLD WOMAN: Monan, listen to me –
MONAN: Ssh! (MONAN *closes his eyes.*) I can see it.
OLD WOMAN: Where?
(MONAN *puts his finger to his forehead.*)
MONAN: Here. (*He points upwards.*) It's in that tree. (*The* OLD WOMAN *looks up.*)
OLD WOMAN: I can't see a bird.
MONAN: In the topmost branches, hidden among the leaves. Am I right?
OLD WOMAN: Yes . . . yes . . . you are . . . I can see it.
MONAN: Good. (MONAN *turns, slowly, towards the bird. He keeps his eyes closed. He throws the spear.*) Did I hit it?
OLD WOMAN: Yes.
(MONAN *opens his eyes.*)
MONAN: Yes! Wait there, mother. I won't be long.
(MONAN *runs off to climb the tree.*)
BOY: He hit the bird with his eyes closed.
ROCK: That's right.
BOY: How?
ROCK: With his eyes closed there was nothing to distract him. He saw only the bird, and his aim was true.
OLD WOMAN: I taught him how to do it. That, and many other things. He's learned well. He's a son any mother could be proud of. Though, sometimes, he's a little too proud himself.
(MONAN *returns, carrying a long, sweeping trail of brightly coloured feathers.*)
MONAN: Look, mother. There are no other feathers like these in all the world.
OLD WOMAN: Is that what you killed the bird for? Its feathers?
MONAN: Yes.
OLD WOMAN: And what will you do with them now you've got them?

MONAN: I don't know . . . I'll wear them, and then everybody will know what a fierce and skilful hunter I am.

OLD WOMAN: It was a stupid thing to do. To kill for the pleasure of it, to satisfy your own desires. A stupid and a dangerous thing!

MONAN: Why?

OLD WOMAN: Life is precious and the taking of it should be serious business.

MONAN: You have them, then. A gift, from me.

OLD WOMAN: I don't want them.

MONAN: Take them!

OLD WOMAN: No!

(MONAN *turns away from her, sulkily.*)

MONAN: What shall I do with them, then?

OLD WOMAN: Give them back to the bird.

MONAN: I can't. It's dead.

OLD WOMAN: To the sky, then.

MONAN: What?

OLD WOMAN: Throw them to the sky.

(MONAN *throws the feathers up.*)

ROCK: So Monan threw the feathers into the sky. They went higher and higher, and, as they rose, a wonderful thing happened.

MONAN: Look, mother! They're growing! They're getting bigger.

ROCK: Bigger and bigger they grew, longer and longer, until, when they had reached the top of the sky, they hung there, a great bow of coloured feathers, stretching out across the world.

STORYTELLER: And we can see them still, to this day, those feathers shining in the sky. And, when we see them, we remember how precious life is.

OLD WOMAN: Monan. Listen to me, now. Everything I've taught you you've learned well. There's no more skilful hunter than you in the world, no one with more courage and wit. But you use all these skills only to amuse yourself. It's time you used them to help others.

MONAN: What others?

OLD WOMAN: People. Out there, in the world, people live, but they live in fear. The world is a terrible place for them, everything in it makes them afraid. You must go and take their fear from them, so that they can walk without fear, and become the keepers of the Earth.

MONAN: You want me to leave you, leave my home?

OLD WOMAN: The world's your home. It was for this I raised you. You will become a great hero. You will heal the sick, and kill demons. You will bring power and strength to people, and teach them how to use it. Your name will be remembered. Go now, with my blessing.

(*She turns to go.*)

MONAN: Mother –

(*She stops.*)

Won't I see you again?

OLD WOMAN: You'll see me. If you need my help, call me, and I'll come.

(*She goes, leaving* MONAN *alone.*)

ROCK: So Monan left his home on top of the mountain and went down into the world. He travelled a long way, until he came to a place where a great river ran through the middle of the forest. But the river was dried up. Where there had been water there was only mud, and the trees on its bank were leafless and dying.

(*Two women enter,* GUIOMAR *and* INKARI. INKARI *leads* GUIOMAR.)

INKARI: Just a few more steps, Guiomar. We're almost there.

GUIOMAR: Is there any water?

INKARI: A little. There's a small pool just here. Kneel down.

(INKARI *helps* GUIOMAR *to kneel. She scoops up the water with her hands and raises it to* GUIOMAR'*s mouth.*)

Now. Drink.

(*The* SHAMAN *enters.*)

SHAMAN: Leave that water! Don't let her drink it!

INKARI: She's thirsty.

SHAMAN: We're all thirsty, but we may not drink. The water is cursed.

INKARI: If she doesn't drink, she'll die.

SHAMAN: Then she must die.

GUIOMAR: He's right, Inkari. He's the shaman, and he speaks the truth.

INKARI: What truth does he speak? I know why he doesn't want you to drink. He wants the water for himself.

SHAMAN: You dare to say that of me?

INKARI: I've seen you drinking here, when you thought no one was looking!

SHAMAN: You lie! I am the shaman – !

INKARI: And I'm the chief's daughter, and I say this old woman shall drink!

(*She raises her hands to* GUIOMAR*'s mouth. The* SHAMAN *steps forward and knocks her away. She cries out.*)

If my father still had his strength –

SHAMAN: But he doesn't. He has no strength. He's weak. And his weakness has brought this curse on us. And, for your insult to me, you deserve to die!

GUIOMAR: So!

(MONAN *steps forward.*)

MONAN: Stop! Leave her! Don't touch her again, or you'll answer to me!

GUIOMAR: Who's that?

INKARI: A man. He came out of the forest. I've never seen him before.

MONAN: My name is Monan. I'm a stranger. What's going on here? What's happened to the river?

INKARI: A year ago, the waters began to sink. We waited for the rains to come and fill it up again, but they haven't come. So the waters grew lower and lower. Now they've almost gone, and the people are dying.

SHAMAN: There's nothing we can do about it. It's the will of Sume. We're being punished for some great wickedness.

GUIOMAR: Yes. I know of a wickedness that was done here –

SHAMAN: Quiet, old woman! You speak nonsense.

MONAN: And you speak too much. Go away from here. Go on. Before I call up my spirits to take you away. (*He roars in the* SHAMAN's *face. The* SHAMAN *runs in terror.*)

Old woman, here.

(MONAN *kneels. He cups water in his hands and gives it to* GUIOMAR. *She drinks.*)

GUIOMAR: Thank you. Your hands are gentle.

MONAN: How long have you been blind?

GUIOMAR: Since I was a young woman.

INKARI: She would have been cast out, but my father forbade it.

SHAMAN: Is she your mother?

INKARI: No. My mother died giving birth to me, but this woman nursed me and raised me.

MONAN: Do you have no children of your own?

GUIOMAR: No. What do you look like? Let me touch your face. Although I am blind I can see with my fingers. (*She runs her hands over* MONAN's *face.*) A strong face. But there is the softness of youth. Proud. And fierce – (*She draws her hands away suddenly, as if they have been burned.*)

MONAN: What is it? What's the matter? What did you see? (GUIOMAR *shakes her head.*)

INKARI: Can you really call up spirits?

MONAN: I don't know. (*He stands.*) But I will bring back the river.

INKARI: You?

MONAN: Yes.

INKARI: How?

MONAN: I don't know that either, yet.

(GUIOMAR *stands.*)

GUIOMAR: He will. I know it. (*To* INKARI) Let us return to your father, now. Tell him that the waters will be coming back. And with the waters, his strength will return.

(*She holds her arm out to* INKARI. INKARI *takes her arm, and leads* GUIOMAR *off.*)

ROCK: Monan went in search of the river, following the dry bed, the thin trickle of muddy water. And as he went, he listened to the songs of the birds, the grunting of the wild pigs, the screeching of the monkeys.

STORYTELLER: Follow us! they cried. We know the way! We know where the river has gone! Follow us, follow us!

ROCK: So he followed them, and they led him to a dark place, deep between high cliffs. And there, in that ravine, he found what it was that had been stealing the river.

(*The* GIANT TOAD *enters.*)

GIANT TOAD: Me.

BOY: A toad!

ROCK: A giant toad, immense and powerful, it squatted there before him on the stones and boulders, drinking the waters of the river.

GIANT TOAD: Once, I was a little toad, no bigger than your thumb. Then I began to drink, and, as I drank, I grew bigger. And the bigger I got, the more I wanted to drink. So I drank and I grew and I grew and I drank. Still I'm not satisfied. I'll go on drinking until I've drunk up all the waters of the world. Then, I'll be the only living thing in the world. I'll be as big as the world itself. I'll crush it beneath my weight, and nothing will exist, only me.

MONAN: You'll get no bigger than you are now. I've come to destroy you.

GIANT TOAD: You? I'd like to see you try.

MONAN: I will!

(MONAN *attacks the* TOAD *with his spear. The* TOAD *knocks him away and laughs.* MONAN *tries again. Again the* TOAD *knocks him away.* MONAN *tries a third time. The* TOAD *knocks him away and roars with laughter.*)

GIANT TOAD: Your little spear can't harm me! Nothing can harm me!

ROCK: He was right. The toad's skin was so thick and tough that no weapon could pierce it.

MONAN: But Monan didn't give up. He attacked the toad again. (MONAN *throws himself at the* TOAD. *He tries to wrestle with it, to pull it off. The* TOAD *is immovable.*)

ROCK: He tried wrestling with it. He pushed and he pulled and he pounded and he pummelled. But he couldn't budge the toad an inch.

(*The* TOAD *throws* MONAN *off.* MONAN *falls.*)

GIANT TOAD: Idiot! There's nothing you can do to me. I'm more powerful than you. I'm the most powerful creature in all the world. And soon I'll be the most powerful creature in the universe.

ROCK: Exhausted, Monan lay on his back. He saw that he had been defeated.

MONAN: It's true. I can't hurt you. I give in.

BOY: He gave up!

ROCK: Yes.

BOY: But –

ROCK: Watch. Listen. The story isn't finished yet.

MONAN: You say that you're going to drink up all the water in the world?

GIANT TOAD: That's right, I am.

MONAN: I'd like to see you do that.

GIANT TOAD: Would you? Very well. Watch, and wonder. It will be the last thing you see.

ROCK: Then the toad began to open its mouth. It opened it wider and wider, blotting out the earth, and the sky, even blotting out the sun. And then, when it had opened its mouth as wide as it would go –

MONAN: – Monan snatched up his spear, and hurled it down the toad's throat, deep into its belly!

(*The* TOAD *gives a terrible roar of anger and pain.*)

ROCK: The toad gave a great roar of pain –

MONAN: – and its skin split –
STORYTELLER: – and its body burst –
ROCK: – and all the water it had drunk came rushing out –
MONAN: – a great torrent, flooding and flowing –
STORYTELLER: – pounding and pouring back along its banks.
ROCK: And, as the river returned, all the frogs that the toad had also swallowed began to sing for joy –
STORYTELLER: – and so they still sing, whenever the rain falls and the river floods, in memory of the time when Monan set them free.
ROCK: And that was how Monan released the waters, and brought life back to the land.
BOY: I've heard the frogs singing when the rain comes and the river rises, but I never knew why. I never even thought there was a reason. I thought they just sang.
ROCK: Nothing happens without reason. There's a reason for everything. All that happens is a story, and inside every story there's a meaning.
BOY: All that happens?
ROCK: Yes.
BOY: Even me, being here?
ROCK: Yes. This too is a story, and has its meaning.
BOY: What is it?
ROCK: You can't know that yet. Your story isn't finished. You may never know it, but others will.
BOY: Tell me more about Monan. Was he welcomed as a hero?
(GUIOMAR *enters.*)
GUIOMAR: As a great hero and saviour.
BOY: Did the chief get his strength back?
(CHIEF *enters.*)
CHIEF: The chief's strength returned, and he became leader of his people again.
BOY: And did he marry Inkari, the chief's daughter, and become chief himself?
(INKARI *enters.*)

INKARI: From the moment she saw him on the river bank, Inkari wanted no one else for her husband.

ROCK: But before that happened, he had to prove himself further.

(*The* SHAMAN *enters.*)

SHAMAN: Who is this man? What do we know about him? He is a stranger.

MONAN: I am Monan –

SHAMAN: Monan. That name means nothing to me. I've never heard it before.

INKARI: He freed the waters. He brought life back to us.

SHAMAN: He is not of our people.

INKARI: He has done more for our people than you have ever done.

CHIEF: Inkari! That's enough! (*To the* SHAMAN) I wish my daughter to marry this man. I wish to adopt him as my son. What must he do to make this possible?

SHAMAN: He must bring us a gift, to show his good intention.

CHIEF: A gift? Yes, that's fair. Are you willing to do this?

MONAN: Name me anything, and I'll bring it to you.

SHAMAN: Then bring us fire.

(*Pause.*)

INKARI: Fire! That's impossible! Father, you know that fire is forbidden to us. It belongs to the Jaguar.

CHIEF: I know that. But he has already promised.

SHAMAN: It's the price he must pay. The price that is asked for.

INKARI: Who asks it?

SHAMAN: I do! (*To* MONAN) Bring us the gift of fire. Prove yourself worthy to take your place among us.

CHIEF: Will you pay this price?

MONAN: Yes.

INKARI: Father!

CHIEF: Quiet! (*To* MONAN) Then, if you bring us fire, I will accept it, and accept you as my son.

GUIOMAR: He will bring it. I see it, burning already in our homes. I feel its heat on my hands and face. What he says he will, is done already.

(INKARI, CHIEF, GUIOMAR *and* SHAMAN *go.*)

ROCK: Now Monan went in search of the Jaguar, who was the keeper of fire, and who lived in the deepest heart of the forest. He took no weapons with him. It was not with the use of weapons that he could take fire. Deeper and deeper he went –

STORYTELLER: – deeper and deeper. He had never been so deep in the forest before. It was dark. Shadows moved. He heard noises and voices.

ROCK: And at last he came to the very centre of the forest. And there, standing before him, between two trees, he saw –

STORYTELLER: – the Jaguar.

(*The* JAGUAR *has entered. It carries a bow and arrows. It faces* MONAN.)

JAGUAR: What are you doing here? Who are you? Why are you hunting in my forest?

MONAN: I am not hunting. Look. I carry no weapons.

JAGUAR: What is your name? Who are your people?

MONAN: My name is . . . Botoque. I have no people.

JAGUAR: Do not move. Stay where you are.

(*The* JAGUAR *walks carefully round* MONAN, *looking him over.*)

BOY: He said his name was Botoque. That was the name his real mother gave him when he was born.

ROCK: It was.

BOY: But he had never heard it. How did he know?

ROCK: It was his name. It was part of him, and it never left him. It made itself known to him when he needed it.

JAGUAR: Why have you come to my forest?

MONAN: I have no other home.

JAGUAR: Men are not welcome here.

MONAN: Am I man? I did not know I was. I do not know what I am.

JAGUAR: Perhaps you are a jaguar, then.
MONAN: Perhaps.
(*The* JAGUAR *holds up the bow and arrows.*)
JAGUAR: Do you know what these are?
MONAN: No. What are they for?
JAGUAR: Do you know who I am?
MONAN: No.
JAGUAR: I could kill you. Don't you fear me?
MONAN: What is fear?
JAGUAR: All I would have to do is leave you here, alone, and death would come and find you.
MONAN: What is death?
JAGUAR: Something you and I do not fear. (*Pause.*) I live alone here. It's not always good to be alone. (*Pause.*) Come with me to my home. We will share the forest together.
MONAN: I'd like that.
JAGUAR: Come with me, then. I'll show you my fire.
MONAN: Fire? What's that? Is it an animal . . . or a bird?
JAGUAR: It is a kind of bird.
ROCK: Monan went with the Jaguar to its home.
JAGUAR: The most beautiful bird in the world.
ROCK: And there the Jaguar fed him, and showed him fire.
JAGUAR: But to those who do not treat it with respect, its feathers are deadly.
ROCK: And as he sat before it, the fire burned into his heart and lit the coals of his eyes.
MONAN: It's beautiful. I've never seen such a thing before.
JAGUAR: Few have. It stays here with me. I am its keeper.
MONAN: Why?
JAGUAR: It is too dangerous to go out into the world.
MONAN: How could such a thing be dangerous?
JAGUAR: Put your hand into it. Feel the sting of its feathers.
(MONAN *puts his hand into the flames. He cries out in pain and draws his hand back.*)
Now you know what fear is, and you have had a small taste of death. Remember it, and think what would

become of the earth if this thing was loosed upon it. (*Pause.*) Now I will show you another wonder. This too carries death and is to be feared. (*The* JAGUAR *takes out an arrow and fits it to the string of the bow.*) You see that tree there, standing taller than all the rest?

MONAN: Yes, I see it.

JAGUAR: On the topmost branch of that tree there is a leaf, a large leaf, standing out from all the others. Do you see that?

MONAN: Yes . . .

JAGUAR: Now watch.

(*The* JAGUAR *takes aim and fires the arrow as the* ROCK *speaks.*)

ROCK: Then the Jaguar took aim and loosed the arrow. The arrow flew through the air and pierced the leaf where it joined on to the branch. The leaf fell to the earth.

MONAN: That is a wonder! With these two things, a man could become the master of the earth.

JAGUAR: Indeed he could. (*Pause.*) Shall I teach you to use this?

MONAN: I'm not sure my hands have the skill.

JAGUAR: The skill is not in the hand that looses the arrow. It is in the eye that guides the arrow to its mark. Here. Try.

(MONAN *takes the bow and an arrow.*)

Fit the arrow to the string.

(MONAN *does so.*)

Raise the bow and draw the string.

(MONAN *does so.*)

Look along the shaft of the arrow to find your mark.

MONAN: What is my mark?

JAGUAR: The leaf next to the one I hit.

(MONAN *takes aim.*)

Now. Loose the arrow.

(MONAN *fires the arrow.*)

ROCK: Monan loosed his arrow. It pierced the leaf and the leaf fell.

JAGUAR: Very good. Your eye does have some skill.

MONAN: I might have been lucky. Give me some more arrows. Let me try again.

(The JAGUAR *hands him the arrows.* MONAN *fits an arrow to the string.)*

Fit the arrow to the string. Raise the bow. Draw back the string. Find my mark . . . and loose the arrow.

(He fires the arrow.)

ROCK: Once more the arrow flew. Once more it pierced a leaf.

MONAN: I'll try another.

(He fits another arrow, fires it.)

And another.

(He fires arrows in rapid succession, calling out in joy and triumph.)

Another! Another! Another! Another!

ROCK: Again and again the arrows flew. Each one found its mark and the leaves fell like rain on to the earth.

JAGUAR: Stop! No more! You'll waste all my arrows, and the tree will have no leaves!

MONAN: There's still one left. One arrow, and one leaf. What shall be my mark this time? The leaf? Or you?

JAGUAR: Me?

MONAN: You make an easier target.

(MONAN *aims the arrow at the* JAGUAR.)

JAGUAR: What are you doing?

MONAN: Do you know what fear is, now? Can you smell it? Is the taste of death in your mouth? Shall I make you swallow it?

JAGUAR: Botoque – !

MONAN: I am not Botoque! I am Monan, and I have brought you a gift. This!

(He fires the arrow. The JAGUAR *cries out and falls.)*

And in return for my gift, I'll take this.

(He holds up the bow.)

And this.

(He walks over to the fire. He pulls a flaming log from the fire

and holds it aloft.)

Fire will go out into the world, and we shall become masters of it.

(*He treads out the rest of the fire.*)

JAGUAR: You are wrong, Monan. You haven't given me death. It is death you carry out into the world. Fire still burns here, in me, my rage and my hatred, which will never die. You shall see it in my eyes, you shall feel it in my teeth and claws. From this time on, I shall prey on you and your children and your children's children. Wherever they go, they will feel my shadow fall across their path, and they will know the true taste of fear.

STORYTELLER: And, from that time, the jaguar has hated man. And it carries the fire that burns in the circles of its eyes, and death in its fangs and claws.

BOY: And now Monan married Inkari and became the chief's son. But did he find out who his real mother was? And what more adventures did he have? What happened next? Tell me.

STORYTELLER: But the Rock said nothing.

BOY: Tell me!

STORYTELLER: It was silent.

BOY: Is that all?

STORYTELLER: The boy shouted in the darkness. He shivered. It was cold.

BOY: Answer me!

STORYTELLER: Nothing stirred. Not a leaf moved. There was no sound.

BOY: It's still night! It's not morning yet! You said you'd tell me all the stories there were. You can't have finished!

STORYTELLER: But the Rock didn't reply. The boy became angry.

BOY: You haven't kept your part of the bargain, so I won't keep mine!

(*He picks up his bow and arrows.*)

These are worth more than your stories. I'll go back to

being a hunter. I'll fire my arrows and the whole forest will fear me!

ROCK: You are Monan's child.

BOY: What?

ROCK: Like him, you would carry death into the world.

BOY: Monan brought life. He freed the waters, he gave fire to people.

ROCK: He didn't give it. There's a price on everything and the price on fire was death. And that was what Monan brought. He couldn't help it. He was Death's son, remember. Listen. There's one more story I have to tell you. And perhaps when you have heard it, you will begin to understand why you came here, and why I'm telling you these stories.

STORYTELLER: So the boy put down his bow and arrows again, and sat on the ground and listened as the Rock told its last story.

MONAN: It told how Monan returned to the people with the fire he had taken, to find that the old chief had died –

INKARI: So he married Inkari and became the new chief, and was hailed as a great warrior and hero –

GUIOMAR: – just as his mother had said he would be, all those years ago. For she knew he was her son who had been lost to her, even though she didn't tell him.

ROCK: And with Monan as their chief, they became a great people, their name was known throughout the world.

MONAN: Their enemies fled from them in fear when he led them into battle.

INKARI: The forest was fat with game, the river was rich with fish.

GUIOMAR: Their children grew strong, their voices were fearless, their eyes were fierce.

SHAMAN: Until death struck them down.

(*The* SHAMAN *moves around and among the other characters, the personification of Death, chanting as if an incantation.*)

It came silent like a jaguar

It came merciless and terrible
It stalked their tracks
In fear they fell before it
Weeping, they cried for mercy
It struck them down
They lay on the earth
Their spirits left them
Their eyes rolled
Their bodies were still
Death walked among them
Restless, hungry.
(GUIOMAR *and* INKARI *huddle together, in fear.*)

INKARI: Help us, Monan.
GUIOMAR: What are we to do?
INKARI: What is this sickness?
GUIOMAR: Where does it come from?
INKARI: Help us!
GUIOMAR: Heal us!
INKARI: Do something!
GUIOMAR: Save us!
SHAMAN: Listen to them, Monan. Do you hear them? These are your people. They call to you. You brought them water, you brought them fire. Did you bring them this as well?
MONAN: No!
SHAMAN: Help them. Heal them. Save them. If you can.
MONAN: I can! I will!
(GUIOMAR *and* INKARI *remain huddled together onstage. The* SHAMAN *stands over them.*)
ROCK: Monan went off alone. He called to his mother, and she came.
(*The* OLD WOMAN *enters.*)
OLD WOMAN: You want my help, Monan?
MONAN: Yes. My people have a sickness –
OLD WOMAN: I know.
MONAN: They want me to help them. I've tried everything you taught me, but nothing works. Still they die.

OLD WOMAN: What do you want me to do?

MONAN: To help me, as you promised you would. Tell me how to cure the sickness.

OLD WOMAN: I can't.

MONAN: Can't?

OLD WOMAN: There is no cure for it.

MONAN: What do you mean?

OLD WOMAN: You brought this sickness on them. It was in you from the beginning.

MONAN: In me!

OLD WOMAN: Yes. I am Death, Monan. You are my son. Through you, I have come into the world, and I shall never leave it.

(*The* OLD WOMAN *walks across to* GUIOMAR.)

Do you know this old woman?

MONAN: Yes.

OLD WOMAN: But do you truly know her? She is the woman who gave birth to you. This is your mother.

(*She speaks to* GUIOMAR.)

Can you see me?

(GUIOMAR *looks at the* OLD WOMAN.)

GUIOMAR: I can!

OLD WOMAN: You know who I am?

GUIOMAR: Yes.

OLD WOMAN: Once, on the banks of the river, you gave me your child. I took him, and now I have come to take you.

GUIOMAR: Monan! My son! Botoque! Save me!

OLD WOMAN: He can't.

(*She touches* GUIOMAR. *Immediately,* GUIOMAR *falls silent and passive. She stands to one side. The* OLD WOMAN *moves to* INKARI.)

Is this your wife?

MONAN: Yes –

OLD WOMAN: She is no longer. She comes with me. She hears my song. She is forgetting who she was. Now, she is my daughter.

MONAN: No!

(*The* OLD WOMAN *touches* INKARI. INKARI *stands, passive.*)

Inkari!

INKARI: Who is Inkari? I have never heard that name. I am not her. I am a shadow. I am a breath of wind in the leaves. Nothing more.

(INKARI *stands beside* GUIOMAR.)

OLD WOMAN: Come with me. We have a long journey to go on.

(*The* OLD WOMAN *starts to lead* GUIOMAR *and* INKARI *off.* MONAN *runs forward to try and stop them. The* SHAMAN *stands in front of him.*)

SHAMAN: Go! You brought us death! Leave here! We don't want you. You have no name, you have no people! Be an outcast, a wanderer, vanish from the world. We turn our backs on you. You are no longer a person.

(*The* SHAMAN *goes.* MONAN *is alone.*)

ROCK: And so, Monan was cast out by his people. He left them and went far away, and from that time he was never seen again in the world.

BOY: Where did he go? What did he do?

MONAN: He searched for an answer to death. He wanted to bring life back into the world. He knew that somewhere there was an answer.

ROCK: He searched long and hard. He travelled through many places. He saw many terrible and wonderful things. And at last he came to a forest where no one lived. And, in the middle of that forest, he sat down, and he began to think.

(MONAN *sits.*)

MONAN: His thoughts took him deep into himself. He travelled the dark paths within him, seeking the answer. He forgot the world beyond. He did not move.

ROCK: He did not speak.

MONAN: He did not breathe.

ROCK: He grew into the earth. He became still, as a stone, as a rock. A long time passed.

MONAN: And, in the end, he found the answer.

(*Pause.*)

BOY: What was it? What was the answer?

(*The* ROCK *does not reply.*)

Tell me. What is the answer to death?

(MONAN *and the* ROCK *are both still, crouched in the same attitude.*)

STORYTELLER: But the rock was silent. It said no more to him. Whatever had been speaking to him had finished. The rock was only a rock.

BOY: The boy stood up. He looked around. Sunlight was shining through the trees. Birds were singing. It was morning, and it was time to go home.

STORYTELLER: So he left his bow and arrows on the ground because he had no more use for them, and went back through the forest to his home.

BOY: But when he came to the place where his home had been, it wasn't there any more.

STORYTELLER: It was gone. His grandmother had gone. His people had gone. There was nothing.

(*The* BOY *calls out.*)

BOY: Grandmother! Where are you? What's happened? Grandmother!

STORYTELLER: The boy walked on, calling, searching. He walked on and on. He didn't know how long he walked for. But at last he came to a river. He was tired and thirsty, so he knelt down by the river to drink. But when he looked into the water –

BOY: – he saw the face of an old man. An old man's face, reflected in the water, where his face should have been.

STORYTELLER: He looked at his hands. They were the hands of an old man. His body was the body of an old man.

BOY: How did I get to be old? What's happened to me?

STORYTELLER: Even as he spoke he understood. The day and night he'd spent listening to the stories, had been his whole life. And now here he was, at the end of his life. His grandmother was dead. All the people he'd ever known were dead. And he had nothing except those stories.

BOY: And the answer to death. Now, I think, I know the answer.

(VILLAGERS *enter as the* STORYTELLER *speaks.*)

STORYTELLER: He walked on until he came to a village. The people of the village didn't know who he was. They looked at him strangely. They asked him questions.

1ST VILLAGER: Who are you?

2ND VILLAGER: Where do you come from?

3RD VILLAGER: Why are you walking alone?

4TH VILLAGER: What do you want here?

BOY: I've brought you a gift.

1ST VILLAGER: A gift? What kind of gift?

2ND VILLAGER: What can an old man like you give us?

BOY: Stories.

3RD VILLAGER: Stories?

4TH VILLAGER: What are stories?

1ST VILLAGER: Are they some kind of food?

2ND VILLAGER: Some kind of weapon?

3RD VILLAGER: We don't know what you're talking about.

4TH VILLAGER: We've never heard of stories. What are they?

BOY: Stories are what you are. They are where you came from and how you were made. Stories are why things are as they are, and how they came to be. They are the whole world, and everything beyond the world, and it's time you knew what they were. Sit. Listen.

(*The* BOY *sits. The* VILLAGERS *sit around him.*)

STORYTELLER: So he sat and began to tell them his stories. And they sat and listened, just as you are listening to me, as all people in the world now sit and listen to stories. For they are stronger than death, and they have come into the world, and will never leave it.

THE END

FIRST PRIZE: UNDER 15

BUFFALO DANCE

by Class 5 (1990)
Ecole Internationale
de Genève

GENEVA
SWITZERLAND

AUTHORS' NOTE

Buffalo Dance faithfully follows the concept of the tale describing the origins of the Blackfeet Indians' traditional Buffalo Dance but differs in some significant ways. The scene is set by the suggestion that some of the Blackfeet warriors have upset the harmony of the tribe and the balance of nature by overhunting the buffalo; this idea is original to this play and is not suggested in the original tale.

In the original story the father is alone when he searches for his daughter and it is he, rather than a brave, who is killed by the buffalo. Also, the buffalo does not accompany the father and daughter back to the camp and there is no mention of the Thunderbird appearing in the Buffalo Dance.

The dance itself was once an important ritual conducted by many of the Plains Indian nations before every major buffalo hunting expedition. Sadly, the dance had become a memory by the 1880s, following the destruction of the last herds of bison and the erosion of the indigenous people's cultural heritage.

The names of the characters are taken from various books researched by the authors. It is interesting to reflect that the majority of the names are those of people who were associated with Chief Sitting Bull before the Wounded Knee tragedy, just 100 years ago.

Characters

Narrator

BLACKFOOT TRIBE

WOUNDED KNEE: Chief
BLACK CLOUD: Shaman
WILD DOG: Warrior
RUNNING DEER: Hunter
CHASE WOUNDED: Hunter
HAWK MAN: Hunter
RED WIND: Hunter
WHITE PLUME: Hunter
MOON STAR: Old woman
LAUGHING WATER: Young girl
TWO FEATHERS: Young girl

WHITE DOVE'S FAMILY

BRAVE THUNDER: Father
SINGING BIRD: Mother
PURPLE DAWN: Grandmother
RED HAWK: brother
WHITE DOVE: Daughter

ANIMALS

BIG HORN: Shaman buffalo
MAGPIE: Animal spirit
THUNDERBIRD: Great spirit

Act 1

Spotlight on NARRATOR *sitting alone.*

NARRATOR. This story takes place long, long ago in North America when the world was young. Our tale begins in a Blackfeet camp one cold winter's morning. The Blackfeet tribe have lived happily on the great plains south of the Saskatchewan river for many moons . . . yet now they are cold, miserable and starving. In fact, they have never fallen on such hard times in living memory.

(NARRATOR *exits right. Lights open on camp. The Blackfeet tribe are clustered around a campfire shivering, rubbing hands and grumbling. Sounds of babies crying.* WILD DOG *struts on to the stage.*)

WILD DOG: Wayeeah! What a noise . . . can't anyone stop the babies from crying! Moon Star, this racket's driving me mad.

MOON STAR: It's driving you mad! And when do you stop to think of anyone else? What about these poor children then, why do you think they're crying? Let me tell you, it's not from happiness, that's for sure.

WILD DOG: Well . . . I . . . I . . .

MOON STAR: (*Rocking a baby*) . . . Look at this Wild Dog! Grass roots and boiled leather soup. Wouldn't you cry if you were a baby and hadn't eaten a good meal for weeks. Poor souls.

WILD DOG: Don't worry, the hunting party will return with buffalo meat before this day ends.

MOON STAR: Huh! You've said the same thing for weeks on end and what have you and your warriors brought home? One old coyote and a skinny rabbit that was blind in one eye. What mighty hunters we have!

(WOUNDED KNEE *enters shivering, rubbing hands.*)

WOUNDED KNEE: Enough of this squabbling. Arguing

amongst ourselves will help no one. The hunters have done their best, there just isn't any buffalo, or any other game for that matter for miles around! We need the help of the Great Spirit Wakantanka before we all starve to death. I've had enough of this! Wild Dog, go and fetch the shaman.

(*Exit* WILD DOG.)

MOON STAR: (*Sobbing*) Look around you Wounded Knee. Do you think Wakantanka cares for us any more? Black Cloud has refused to try to talk to the spirits since last summer . . . will he help us now?

WOUNDED KNEE: I really don't know Moon Star. But let's not give up hope.

(*Enter* BLACK CLOUD *and* WILD DOG.)

BLACK CLOUD: Ha ha, (*grim laugh*) I had an idea you'd be calling for my help again.

WOUNDED KNEE: Black Cloud, we can't last much longer without the spirits help! Have they deserted us? What's happening? Never before has there been such hunger among our people. If we don't catch some game soon we'll not survive the winter.

BLACK CLOUD: (*Angrily*) You want my help? You've got the nerve to ask me for help! Last summer I warned you what would happen if we changed our ways. I told you that we should always look on all animals as our brothers and sisters. To treat them with respect and never to kill more than we need, but did you listen? Oh no!

(SHAMAN *walks to tepee and holds up a skin.*)

Look at this pile of untreated buffalo skins, but where's the winter meat? I'll tell you where, it's out there on the plain still rotting where Wild Dog and his warriors left it while they went out to kill even more buffalo. What madness! Why kill animals for no reason? And what do we have to show for their greed . . . nothing but a pile of rotting skins, empty bellies and miles of empty land! (*Throws skin to the floor in disgust.*) If you were buffalo and you were treated this way would you return?

WILD DOG: Enough of this, old man. We're just having a run of bad luck, you wait and see. The hunting party will be back soon with enough fresh meat to last us through the winter.

WOUNDED KNEE: I really hope you're right Wild Dog, but I doubt that we'll see any meat from your hunters today . . . or any day for that matter. The buffalo have gone. Black Cloud, is there anything you can do to bring the buffalo back to our lands?

BLACK CLOUD: Possibly. I'll try . . . but if they return will you wipe out the herds as you did last summer?

WOUNDED KNEE: No, no. Never again!

ALL: (*Pleading*) Yes, please help, please help . . .

BLACK CLOUD: All right, all right! I'll try something but I'm not promising that it will work. Where's White Dove? I'll need some help collecting herbs.

RED HAWK: White Dove set out early this morning to look for berries on the great cliff.

SINGING BIRD: Oh I do wish she wouldn't always wander off on her own like this!

WILD DOG: Hah! Wounded Knee, our worries are over. Look over there. It's the hunting party. (*Turning towards* BLACK CLOUD.) It looks like we will not need your help after all, old man.

(RUNNING DEER *enters camp, exhausted*.)

RUNNING DEER: Buffalo, Buffalo, we've found buffalo!

ALL: (*Celebrating*) Hooray, hooray!

PURPLE DAWN: But Running Deer, why are you weeping? Aren't you happy that we'll now all have enough to eat?

RUNNING DEER: Of course I'm happy that there's buffalo . . . but I fear that we may never eat buffalo meat again.

WILD DOG: Why? What are you talking about? Wherever there's buffalo, there's food.

RUNNING DEER: Yes, that's always been true . . . but no longer. When we threw our spears and shot our arrows we didn't even scratch the buffalo.

WOUNDED KNEE: That's impossible!

RUNNING DEER: Impossible? No, this is true! The buffalo were unharmed even when we shot our arrows from close range.

(CHASE WOUNDED *enters camp with the hunting party.*)

CHASE WOUNDED: What Running Deer says is true. The buffalo are protected. We didn't manage to kill a single buffalo!

WOUNDED KNEE: And where are these protected buffalo now?

CHASE WOUNDED: They're at the top of the great cliff. You know, the place where we always stampede the buffalo so that they fall on to the rocks below.

WOUNDED KNEE: Well? Didn't you try to stampede them?

CHASE WOUNDED: Of course we did. We tried everything but they took no notice of us. They didn't even look up!

SINGING BIRD: Oh no. White Dove's at the cliff. Hawk Man, did you see her?

HAWK MAN: Yes, yes, we met her close to the buffalo herd. But don't worry, the buffalo won't harm her. They take no notice of humans.

CHASE WOUNDED: Or arrows and spears!

WHITE PLUME: Singing Bird, White Dove told us to tell you that she'll come back to camp before the sun is overhead.

SINGING BIRD: (*Wringing hands*) Oh, I do hope so.

(MAGPIE *climbs on to a rock behind the crowd.*)

WOUNDED KNEE: Well, Black Cloud, what do we do now? We've found buffalo but are powerless to hunt them.

BLACK CLOUD: A good question. This is really serious, I've never heard of anything like this before. The animals must be protected by Wakantanka.

MAGPIE: Quite right, Shaman!

(*Everyone looks around and all except* BLACK CLOUD *drop to the floor, faces to the ground.*)

BLACK CLOUD: Magpie! What brings you here?

MAGPIE: (*Angrily*) Black Cloud, a great deal has changed in our world since I saw you last!

BLACK CLOUD: Yes. I know, our warriors . . .

MAGPIE: (*Walking around the bodies*) Yes, I know exactly what has been going on. I thought that you human beings considered yourselves as part of this world – as brothers and sisters of all the animals. But in truth you have become destroyers! Do you plan to destroy all the animals that clothe and feed you?

BLACK CLOUD: No, no . . .

MAGPIE: Then how do you plan to change your ways?

BLACK CLOUD: We're lost, Magpie! In which direction should we turn, what should we do?

MAGPIE: Well, here is something most strange to think about . . . I bring you both good and bad news. The good news is that the buffalo have fallen into the ravine and there is enough meat to feed the Blackfeet throughout the winter.

(*Tribe rises, cheering.*)

WOUNDED KNEE: Quiet, quiet all of you! This is good news indeed, but . . . tell us, Magpie, what's the bad news?

MAGPIE: Aaah yes. This news is not so good. White Dove has joined the world of the buffaloes.

SINGING BIRD: (*Falling in front of* MAGPIE) What do you mean, Magpie?

MAGPIE: She has become the wife of a most powerful bull buffalo. The buffalo is also a shaman and is known to all the buffalo as Big Horn.

(PURPLE DAWN *and* SINGING BIRD *cry and wail.*)

BRAVE THUNDER: Magpie, I am Brave Thunder and the father of White Dove. I respect you deeply but I doubt your story. Humans don't marry buffaloes, my daughter could never become the wife of a buffalo!

MAGPIE: I'm sorry, Brave Thunder, she didn't plan to marry a buffalo at all. She . . .

RED HAWK: Magpie, where's this buffalo and my sister now?

White Dove must be saved! (*Turning to* WILD DOG.) Wild Dog, go and fetch our weapons!

BRAVE THUNDER: Stop! Wait! Red Hawk, I know you want your sister returned but first let's learn more about this buffalo. Magpie . . . please tell us exactly what happened.

MAGPIE: Well, after the hunters told your daughter that the buffalo herd could not be forced over the cliff she thought she would try to trick them. You know that she can speak the languages of many animals.

MOON STAR: Yes, we all know that she has this skill.

MAGPIE: Well, she climbed down into the ravine at the bottom of the cliff and called up, 'Buffaloes, listen well. I will marry any buffalo that is brave enough to join me down here.' Of course, she thought this was a clever trick and that all the buffaloes would kill themselves so there would be enough meat to feed all of you. So . . . so . . .

PURPLE DAWN: Don't stop there! Go on! I want to know what's happened to my granddaughter.

MAGPIE: So she called up to the buffalo and told them that she would marry any buffalo who was brave enough to jump down into the ravine and . . .

SINGING BIRD: Yes, yes . . .

MAGPIE: Over fifty buffaloes leapt straight over the cliff and they were killed immediately. Well, almost all. All but one! One of the biggest buffalo I have ever seen actually survived the fall. He climbed out of the pile of buffaloes at the bottom of the cliff and walked straight up to White Dove and said, 'My name is Big Horn. I am the Shaman of the Buffalo and I claim you as my wife. Climb on to my back for we must leave this place of sadness.'

RED HAWK: Didn't White Dove try to run away?

MAGPIE: No, she had given her word and you know White Dove: she respects the animal world and would never break a promise. So . . . you have gained much meat but you have also lost your favourite daughter.

BLACK CLOUD: (*To* CHIEF *and* WILD DOG) If only you had listened to me last summer this would never have . . .

WILD DOG . . . Oh stop complaining! What is done is done.

MAGPIE: He's right, you know. None of this would've happened if you and your warriors hadn't been so greedy.

WOUNDED KNEE: We know that and we're sorry! Come on, let's stop arguing! We have to find a way to save White Dove.

WILD DOG: I say we take her back by force.

BRAVE THUNDER: (*To* WILD DOG) No, no! She's my daughter, I must go alone and try and bring her back myself. I think the buffalo have seen quite enough of you and your hunters.

MAGPIE: I agree, you must use cunning rather than force if possible.

WOUNDED KNEE: Magpie, will you help?

MAGPIE: Yes, but all the Blackfeet must promise one thing.

WOUNDED KNEE: Magpie, all the Blackfeet love White Dove and wish her to return to her own people. Tell us, what is this promise you speak of?

MAGPIE: It is very simple. Remember, once the Blackfeet always spoke to an animal saying 'thou', or 'you'. Then the animals were not just an 'it', something to be used or destroyed and thrown away. Do you remember those days when humans and animals lived together in harmony?

WOUNDED KNEE: Yes. We all remember those good days before the summer madness.

MAGPIE: Well, I only ask that you return to your old ways and continue to speak of all creatures as thou . . . as friends. After all . . . humans are neither superior or inferior to us animals. We animals also have the right to live on this land. Is it too much to ask you to respect the spirits of the land, air and water? Let us live in harmony again!

WOUNDED KNEE: We will, Magpie, I promise you. We

certainly will return to the old ways.
(*Tribe voices support.*)
Magpie, the Blackfeet have no wish to destroy the animal world . . . your world is our world. (*Looking around.*) Is there anyone among the Blackfeet that disagrees with these words? (*Looking at* WILD DOG.)

WILD DOG: No, I agree with you. I am ashamed to admit that my warriors and I acted wrongly last summer. We shall never do so again!
(*All hunters agree.*)

WOUNDED KNEE: Good! Then let us all smoke the pipe of peace to seal this promise forever.
(*Everyone settles around the fire. Drum beats. The peace pipe is ceremonially passed around.*)

MAGPIE: (*Rising*) I am pleased and happy to offer the Blackfeet my help. (*Turning to* BRAVE THUNDER.) Brave Thunder, I am going to search for White Dove and Big Horn now. I'll meet you by those trees before the sun is overhead. (*Leading* BRAVE THUNDER *to one side.*) While I am away you must try to speak to the Great Spirit Wakantanka. Ask the Shaman, Black Cloud, to help you.

BRAVE THUNDER: Thank you, Magpie, I'll set off at once.
(BRAVE THUNDER *goes to say farewell to his family.*)

MAGPIE: Wounded Knee, I hope the next time we meet we'll have White Dove with us. Until then, farewell.
(BRAVE THUNDER *says farewell to his family and* WILD DOG *and exits stage left with the* SHAMAN. MAGPIE *flies off from boulder.*)

WOUNDED KNEE: Good luck, Brave Thunder. Farewell Magpie and thank you! Phew, what a morning . . . OK back to work. Collect your baskets, we should bring back some of the buffalo meat that's lying at the bottom of the cliff. We'll have a feast tonight thanks to White Dove. But before we go let me remind you that only Brave Thunder is to seek his daughter. Do not forget these words, (*turning to* WILD DOG *and* RED HAWK) especially you two!

(*Camp empties except for* WILD DOG, CHASE WOUNDED *and* RED HAWK.)

WILD DOG: Red Hawk, are you going to let your father set off alone? We should find White Dove, Brave Thunder's too old for a task like this, even with Magpie's help.

RED HAWK: Yes, yes, I know! Who wouldn't have a problem fighting a buffalo that can leap down cliffs! Of course I must help him, but why are you so keen to help?

WILD DOG: Two very simple reasons. First of all, I've got a terrible feeling that if I don't do something to make up for my past mistakes my name might very well be changed from Wild Dog to Mad Dog!

CHASE WOUNDED: You could be right! But what's your second reason?

WILD DOG: The second reason? Ah, that's a secret that is firmly locked in my heart. Maybe one day I'll share this secret with you but first we must rescue White Dove.

RED HAWK: Well, I don't know about your secret but I thank you for your offer of help. What about you Chase Wounded, will you join us?

CHASE WOUNDED: Have you already forgotten what the Chief said? He will not be too happy when he discovers that we've gone to help your father. But . . . of course I'll help! Besides, when have you ever known me to turn down an adventure?

RED HAWK: Thank you, my friends.

WILD DOG: Remember, we all went through the Sun Dance together, we are brothers and bound to help you. Sssh, look! (*Pointing offstage.*) There's your father by those trees. (*The three* WARRIORS *hide behind a boulder*.)

BRAVE THUNDER: (*Off stage*) Oh Great Spirit Wakantanka, please listen to my words. We are sorry for what happened last summer. I offer you anything in exchange for White Dove's safe return. (*Sobbing*.) How can you let the buffalo take my one and only daughter? Great One, speak to me, show me some sign that you have heard my words.

(*Lights dim, lightning flashes with noise of thunder.*

WILD DOG, CHASE WOUNDED *and* RED HAWK *rise after noise fades and lights rise.*)

WILD DOG: (*Cowering*) Ayeeah, what a noise! Is your father all right?

RED HAWK: Yes, yes, he's over there staring up at the sky. Did you hear that thunder . . . was that Wakantanka speaking to my father?

WILD DOG: (*Looking around, scanning the horizon*) Who knows! It could have been the voice of the Great Spirit . . .

CHASE WOUNDED: (*Pulling cape tighter around shoulders*) Or it could have been a buffalo stampede. We live in strange times!

RED HAWK: Ssh! Brave Thunder's coming this way, get down!

(*The* WARRIORS *hide behind a boulder.* MAGPIE *and* BRAVE THUNDER *enter.*)

BRAVE THUNDER: Well, Magpie, what should we do now? I tried to speak to Wakantanka. I just hope he heard me.

MAGPIE: I believe he did. I found Big Horn and White Dove almost immediately after I left you! A great wind carried me swiftly through the air straight to where the buffalo and your daughter are resting. They're no more than a half a day's walk from here but I couldn't get close enough to talk to her. Big Horn guards her closely.

BRAVE THUNDER: Excellent news! Which way should we travel?

MAGPIE: Due west. This way, Brave Thunder.

(MAGPIE *and* BRAVE THUNDER *exit stage left. The three* WARRIORS *rise.*)

RED HAWK: Quick, go and collect your weapons. We'll meet by the trees and follow my father's tracks. Be careful.

(WARRIORS *go, lights dim. Spotlight on* NARRATOR. *Set change during the narration.*)

NARRATOR: The three warriors successfully followed the tracks of Brave Thunder and Magpie without being spotted. After all, the tracks were easy to follow in the snow. The braves eventually reached a broad valley which had a stream running quietly along its length. At this point the tracks in the snow changed to show that Brave Thunder had dropped on all fours to crawl to some bushes in the distance. Red Hawk, Wild Dog and Chase Wounded, realizing that Big Horn must be close by, prepared their weapons. With great care, the warriors slowly crept toward a pile of boulders. From this point they had a good view of Brave Thunder and Magpie who were looking intently at two figures lying asleep by the stream.

Act 2

Lights rise. BRAVE THUNDER *and* MAGPIE *are lying behind bushes, stage left.* WILD DOG, CHASE WOUNDED *and* RED HAWK *are hiding behind boulders, stage right.* BIG HORN *and* WHITE DOVE *are lying asleep, centre stage.*

BRAVE THUNDER: That Buffalo is huge!

MAGPIE: Yes, he's the biggest I've ever seen . . . there's no way that he'll just hand over White Dove without an argument!

BRAVE THUNDER: So what should we do? He'll wake up if we try to carry her off.

MAGPIE: Quite right. Wait here, I'll try and speak to White Dove.

BRAVE THUNDER: OK . . . be careful.

MAGPIE: I will. (*Legs shaking as he creeps towards* WHITE DOVE.)

MAGPIE: White Dove. Wake up. Wake up.

WHITE DOVE: What? Oh, Magpie!

MAGPIE: Sssh. I've come to help you.

WHITE DOVE: Oh, Magpie, what can I do, if we were to run

away Big Horn would quickly catch up with us. Big Horn is my husband now and I must obey his wishes.

MAGPIE: Don't you want to escape and return to your own people?

WHITE DOVE: Yes, of course I do. But what can we do? Big Horn is terrifying when he's angry. He's so strong!

MAGPIE: Sssh, not so loud! Your father's waiting for you over by that tree, come.

(BIG HORN *yawns and wakes.* MAGPIE *retreats to the tree.* WHITE DOVE *lies down.*)

BIG HORN: White Dove, are you awake? I could have sworn I heard voices. Were you sleep talking or was I dreaming?

WHITE DOVE: You were dreaming, Big Horn. Close your eyes and go back to sleep.

BIG HORN: Yes, I will try to sleep, this sunshine's good! But first please fetch me some water from the spring.

WHITE DOVE: Very well.

(WHITE DOVE *walks towards the tree.* BIG HORN *yawns, falls asleep and snores.*)

WHITE DOVE: (*Throwing her arms around her father*) Oh Father!

BRAVE THUNDER: White Dove, it is good to see you. Are you well? Has the buffalo mistreated you?

WHITE DOVE: Don't worry, Father. Big Horn has been good to me. He wouldn't harm me. But he's not happy with the Blackfeet people, you must go quickly. He'll kill you if you stay here!

BRAVE THUNDER: The Blackfeet understand why the buffalo are angry . . .

MAGPIE: Enough, you can talk more later. We must think of a way to escape before he wakes up. Oh no . . . look!

(BRAVE THUNDER *and* MAGPIE *hide.* BIG HORN *rises to his feet, looking around.*)

BIG HORN: White Dove, where are you, where's my water?

WHITE DOVE: (*Returning to* BIG HORN) Here it is, Big Horn.

BIG HORN: (*Stoops to drink but suddenly lifts his head, sniffing the air*) I can smell humans!

WHITE DOVE: Impossible! I'm the only human in this valley.

BIG HORN: (*Looking around angrily*) No! I can smell humans! Where are they?

(BIG HORN *walks to stage right.* BRAVE THUNDER *steps out behind* BIG HORN *and raises his bow and arrow.*)

WILD DOG: Look at your father! Doesn't he realize that any buffalo that can jump off a cliff and survive is unlikely to even notice an arrow shot. Chase Wounded, quick, creep up and stop Brave Thunder from loosing that arrow. Red Hawk, go and keep Magpie quiet.

CHASE WOUNDED: Right!

RED HAWK: (*To* WILD DOG) Good luck.

WILD DOG: Thanks . . . (*to himself*) I'll need it!

(*The two creep off and draw* MAGPIE *and* BRAVE THUNDER *to the ground behind the bushes. The noise attracts* BIG HORN'*s attention.*)

BIG HORN: Ah humans! You dare to try to sneak up on me! Have you come to try to steal my rightful wife? Come out where I can see you!

(BIG HORN *paws the ground with* WHITE DOVE *clinging to his neck.*)

WHITE DOVE: Big Horn. Please, please spare them!

BIG HORN: Like they spared my herds last summer? No, this is revenge . . . an eye for an eye!

WHITE DOVE: No. No!!! Forgive them.

(WILD DOG *leaps between the tree and* BIG HORN.)

WHITE DOVE: (*Surprised and happy*) Wild Dog . . . What are you doing here!

BIG HORN: Ah, don't I recognize that name?

WILD DOG: Big Horn, wait! The Blackfeet are truly sorry for what happened last summer. It shall never . . .

BIG HORN: . . . you expect me to listen to you? Now I remember, you were the leader of the hunters!

(BIG HORN *cries with rage, shakes* WHITE DOVE *off and charges* WILD DOG. WHITE DOVE *screams.* WILD DOG *falls.* WHITE DOVE *runs to* WILD DOG, *crying.*)

Are there any more humans to deal with?
(MAGPIE *steps out*.)

BIG HORN: Magpie! What brings you here? I have no quarrel with you.

MAGPIE: And I have no quarrel with you, Big Horn. Please listen to me . . . what Wild Dog had to say was true. The humans really do regret last summer's killings. It will never happen again!

BIG HORN: I find that really hard to believe.

MAGPIE: I can understand that. But trust me, I've heard their words and smoked the peace pipe with them. I am certain they'll never repeat last summer's madness again!

BIG HORN: Magpie, I have no reason not to trust you . . . and I have to admit this young man did not try to harm me or even try to protect himself.

WHITE DOVE: (*Crying*) He sacrificed his life trying to save me.

BIG HORN: Hm. It seems that human beings may have feelings after all. I might just have been just a little hasty.

WHITE DOVE: Magpie, he isn't breathing . . .
(WHITE DOVE *covers* WILD DOG *with her cape and runs to* BIG HORN.)
Big Horn, let me try to bring him back to life.

BIG HORN: I can see that you care for this young man. Yes, you may try, but what makes you think you can succeed?

WHITE DOVE: I really don't know, but something inside me tells me I must try.
(WHITE DOVE *stands and calls on Wakantanka.* MAGPIE *joins in chanting, both perform a dance. Lights dim, drums sound. During the dance* WILD DOG *dresses in bright, clean clothes under the cape. Thunder sounds. Lights rise and* WILD DOG *slowly stands up.*)

BIG HORN: Incredible! Amazing! I didn't realize humans had such powers.

WHITE DOVE: (*Weeping with happiness*) Wild Dog, you're alive!

WILD DOG: (*Shaking his head*) White Dove! What happened to me? The last thing I remember was a massive buffalo running over me!

(BRAVE THUNDER, CHASE WOUNDED *and* RED HAWK *appear from behind tree.* BIG HORN *turns to charge.*)

BRAVE THUNDER: Peace, Big Horn! Look, we come in peace.

(BRAVE THUNDER, CHASE WOUNDED *and* RED HAWK *quickly throw their weapons to the ground.* WHITE DOVE *runs to* BRAVE THUNDER, RED HAWK *and* CHASE WOUNDED.)

WHITE DOVE: Father! Red Hawk! Chase Wounded. It is so good to see you. (*Turning to* BIG HORN.) Big Horn, my father and brother mean no harm.

(CHASE WOUNDED *runs to* WILD DOG.)

BIG HORN: I thought we were not alone. Yes, I can see that you come in peace. I will spare your lives but tell me humans, can you always bring the dead back to life?

BRAVE THUNDER: No, Big Horn, to my knowledge this has never happened before.

MAGPIE: Yes, and I doubt that it will ever happen again!

(BIG HORN *turns towards* WHITE DOVE.)

BIG HORN: White Dove, I can see that you deeply love these people. You humans are more caring than I wanted to believe. You have my permission to return to your people on one condition.

WHITE DOVE: Yes, Big Horn? What is this condition?

BIG HORN: The Blackfeet must learn the buffalo dance and I will be their teacher.

WILD DOG: We are grateful that you will let White Dove return but why do you want to teach us a dance?

WOUNDED KNEE: I have never seen or even heard of this Buffalo Dance before. What's its purpose?

BIG HORN: Ahh, only the buffalo know of this dance. It is an ancient ritual that frees the spirits of buffalo killed in a hunt.

WHITE DOVE: But where do these freed spirits go to, Big Horn?

BIG HORN: They return to earth. This dance must be performed before you set out on a buffalo hunt. So, if you kill any buffalo on your hunt, their freed spirits will be able to return to earth to be with their family and friends. If you perform the Buffalo Dance the buffalo will never disappear from these great plains.

WILD DOG: You must teach us this dance, Big Horn. But where . . . here?

BIG HORN: No, in your camp of course! All the warriors should learn this dance. I should have nothing to fear from the Blackfeet now . . . should I?

WILD DOG and FRIENDS: No, of course not. Come with us . . . this way.

(*All exit with* WHITE DOVE *riding* BIG HORN.)

Act 3

LAUGHING WATER *and* TWO FEATHERS *on stage tending the fire.*

TWO FEATHERS: Pass me those twigs please, the fire's almost gone out.

LAUGHING WATER: Here you are . . . hey, look over there, Two Feathers, some people are coming this way.

TWO FEATHERS: I can't see as well as you, Laughing Water. Who are they?

LAUGHING WATER: No idea. There are five people and . . . one of them is riding a buffalo!

TWO FEATHERS: You're seeing things. People don't ride buffaloes!

LAUGHING WATER: Oh don't they? Look over there, can't you see?

TWO FEATHERS: Yes, you're right . . . quick, call Wounded Knee.

(TWO FEATHERS *runs off calling for* WOUNDED KNEE. LAUGHING WATER *picks up a spear. The whole tribe enters.*)

WOUNDED KNEE: Calm down, everyone! Moon Star, what's going on?

TWO FEATHERS: Wounded Knee, look for yourself. Over there!

WOUNDED KNEE: How strange! A human on a buffalo! Is this more of your magic, Black Cloud?

SHAMAN: No, not at all . . .

SINGING BIRD: It's White Dove and my husband . . . that buffalo must be Big Horn!

WOUNDED KNEE: That accounts for two people but who are the other three? (*Looking around.*) Where's Wild Dog? Wild Dog?

SINGING BIRD: And Red Hawk!

WOUNDED KNEE: Didn't I forbid anyone to leave the camp except Brave Thunder? Why I'll, I'll . . .

(MAGPIE *enters and sits on boulder.*)

MAGPIE: Don't be so hasty, Wounded Knee, wait until you hear what they have to say.

WOUNDED KNEE: Aaa, Magpie!

SINGING BIRD: Is White Dove all right . . . ?

PURPLE DAWN: Has Big Horn freed her . . . ?

WOUNDED KNEE: Why is Big Horn coming here?

MAGPIE: Stop! Your questions will all be answered soon. Look, here they come.

(WHITE DOVE, BRAVE THUNDER, RED HAWK, CHASE WOUNDED *and* WILD DOG *enter the camp.* WHITE DOVE *runs to* SINGING BIRD *and* PURPLE DAWN.)

WOUNDED KNEE: Greetings, Brave Thunder, it is good to see you and your daughter alive and well. As for you three, go to my tepee! I'll speak with you later . . .

MAGPIE: Wounded Knee, I really think you should listen to the words of Big Horn before you punish your braves.

WOUNDED KNEE: You think so? We'll see, stop there you three! Well, where is this Big Horn?

WHITE DOVE: He's waiting over by those trees but he doesn't want to enter the camp without a promise that he'll not be harmed.

WOUNDED KNEE: Did he harm you in any way, White Dove?

WHITE DOVE: No, he treated me well . . .
WOUNDED KNEE: And does he still consider you his wife?
WHITE DOVE: No, I am free to leave him, but . . .
BRAVE THUNDER: Wounded Knee, why don't you let Big Horn speak for himself? Let the buffalo enter the camp, he has important news for all the Blackfeet.
WOUNDED KNEE: Very well! White Dove, please go and tell Big Horn that he is welcome in this camp.
(WHITE DOVE *exits stage left.*)
Two Feathers go and get my headdress and spear. Now, (*turning to the three braves*) you three. Please tell me why you disobeyed me when I told you not to look for White Dove?
BRAVE THUNDER: Wounded Knee, don't be angry with those men. If it wasn't for my son and his friends, especially Wild Dog, I would probably not be alive today.
(*Enter* WHITE DOVE *riding* BIG HORN.)
BIG HORN: What Brave Thunder says is true. When I learned that a human was near my camp I remembered the summer madness when your people destroyed my herds. I was angry and would have charged and killed Brave Thunder but Wild Dog sacrificed his life to protect the old hunter.
BLACK CLOUD: But if this is true, why isn't he dead?
BIG HORN: White Dove and Magpie here performed a dance and brought him back to life. I know this is hard to believe, but it is true.
MAGPIE: It most certainly is true. With the help of Wakantanka, we did indeed bring Wild Dog back to life.
WOUNDED KNEE: Wakantanka has looked on us kindly, this is a tale that will be told around the campfire for many moons! So, it seems that our three braves are heroes after all. But tell me Big Horn, what brings you to our camp?
BIG HORN: Well, until Wild Dog sacrificed his life to protect Brave Thunder I did not realize that human beings really had feelings and cared for one another. I'm sure you can

understand my point of view. Imagine how you would have felt if you had seen your family and friends killed for absolutely no reason! But . . . I have been promised that the Blackfeet will never slaughter our buffalo herds again. Is this really true?

WOUNDED KNEE: As certain as the sun that rises every morning.

ALL: (*In chorus*) Yes.

BIG HORN: Then I will teach you the powerful Buffalo Dance. This is a dance that you must always perform before you set off on a buffalo hunt if you wish to have good hunting.

BLACK CLOUD: But how will this dance help us . . . or you?

BIG HORN: Simple! The dance frees the spirits of all the buffaloes killed in a hunt so that they may return to earth to be with their families and friends.

WOUNDED KNEE: So the buffalo herds will never become smaller, wonderful!

BIG HORN: Right!

WOUNDED KNEE: Then we'd be pleased to learn this dance!

BLACK CLOUD: Big Horn, what do we need to perform this ceremony? Come let us prepare ourselves . . .

(BIG HORN *and* BLACK CLOUD *move behind tepee.*)

WOUNDED KNEE: And we will clear a space for the dance to take place. Men, get rid of those skins, collect your weapons and put on your war paint. Women, clear the space of these pots and baskets, put on your finest clothes. Bring out the drums! Light up the fire!

(*Dance begins, led by* BIG HORN. *The drum/chant tempo builds up and the lights dim to leave a red spotlight illuminating the rear boulders.* THUNDERBIRD *rises on to boulders with wings raised, swaying to the rhythm of the music. Suddenly all music and chanting stops. Thunder and lightning mask* THUNDERBIRD'*s exit. Lights rise.*)

BIG HORN: Wounded Knee, did you see the Thunderbird dancing with us!

WOUNDED KNEE: Yes, I did! It is rare for Wakantanka to allow the Thunderbird to visit the world of humans.

BIG HORN: Yes, indeed. It is good to have man, the animals and the spirits back in harmony again!

WOUNDED KNEE: Too true! Well, Big Horn where will you go now?

BIG HORN: I'm not sure . . . tell me, Wounded Knee, have you ever ridden a buffalo?

WOUNDED KNEE: No, never. Why?

BIG HORN: Well, why not try? Come on, climb up on my back and come and visit some of my herds out on the plains.

WOUNDED KNEE: My friend, why not?

(WOUNDED KNEE *leaps on to* BIG HORN'*s back*.)

. . . let's go!

(BIG HORN *moves offstage, followed by the Blackfeet tribe cheering*. WHITE DOVE *and* WILD DOG *remain on stage*.)

WHITE DOVE: Wild Dog, thank you once again for saving my father's life.

WILD DOG: Well, it was the least I could do . . . after all, you were ready to live with a buffalo for the rest of your life so that we could all be fed.

WHITE DOVE: Anyway, our problems are now over and this story ends happily. We now have the Buffalo Dance so the buffalo spirits are safe and free.

WILD DOG: Yes, and there will always be buffalo to clothe and feed us. It is good to know that the Blackfeet will always share these lands with Big Horn's mighty herds of buffalo!

(*Short pause*.)

WHITE DOVE: (*Shyly*) Wild Dog, can I ask you a question?

WILD DOG: Of course! Ask away.

WHITE DOVE: Red Hawk told me you had a deep secret and I just wondered, well . . .

WILD DOG: Mmm?

WHITE DOVE: Well I just wondered if . . . Oh, please tell me your secret?

WILD DOG: White Dove, you are the only one I would ever share my secret with. But not here. (*Looking around at the audience.*) You never know who might be listening! Let's go somewhere quiet.

(*Exit* WHITE DOVE *and* WILD DOG. *Lights fade. Curtain closes.*)

THE END

JOINT SECOND PRIZE: 15 AND OVER

CHIPKO

A Play for Outdoors

by Ecole d'Humanité

Sarah, Lottie, Stefan, Alain, Kara, Regula, Peggy, Helen, Nina, Maggie, Ursi, Ellen, Ivo, Sarah, Brian, Emmanuel, Angelo, Jan, Lise, Scott, Melissa

HASLIBERG-GOLDERN, SWITZERLAND

This play uses giant puppets in the 'Bread and Puppet theatre' style

AUTHORS' NOTE
Why 'Chipko'?

The Himalayas were originally densely forested on their lower slopes up to an elevation of over 4000 metres, but in the last century they have suffered from widespread deforestation and are now the scene of one of the most serious ecological disasters in the world. Uncontrolled logging for industrial purposes has led to massive soil erosion on the steep slopes and this is experienced downstream in the plains of India and Bangladesh as devastating floods.

The local people who used the forests sustainably for centuries before commercial exploitation began, noticed the correlation between the logging and the floods and in 1973 started hugging the trees to prevent them from being felled. This action has now spread throughout the Himalayas as the highly effective Chipko movement, involving mostly women, as it is they who collect firewood and water and hence suffer most from the effects of deforestation.

As a result the government of Uttar Pradesh has placed a moratorium on the commercial felling of trees above an altitude of 1000 metres and on slopes greater than 30 degrees. The Chipko movement is now following up this success with village-based reforestation schemes and a campaign against the proposed Tehri Dam which would flood 90 villages and thousands of hectares of fertile land.

GIANT PUPPETS

Goddess (a tree/earth mother)
Six Chipko women
Trees (can just be symbolic long sail of green cloth)
The city (six tower blocks that can move around)
Monster (a tree-felling machine)
Three white birds

MASKED PERFORMERS

Grey men (of the city)

MUSICIANS

Cellist and violinist
(or whoever is available)

SETTING

The open air

Note: The power of Bread and Puppet theatre owes much to the large scale of the puppets and their movements, even just the tilting of a giant head.

Scene 1

Performers dressed in white come together from behind trees and bushes making music with bells, stones rubbing together, rattles – quiet, weird music. They form a circle around their GODDESS and sing to her a song of praise. They leave silently, reverently, and the story begins.

Scene 2

Five TREES stand regally and the six CHIPKO WOMEN PUPPETS come singing the song 'Standing Like a Tree', accompanied by a single violin. As they come nearer, everyone starts to sing the song, those holding the TREES and the GODDESS too.

When my roots are down
My heart is wide and open
Come down the rain
Come down the sun
Come down the fruit
To the heart that is open
To be standing like a tree.
(*Repeats*)

The song stops when the CHIPKO WOMEN are in front of the TREES and the TREES and the WOMEN bow to each other and interlock together as a symbol of their closeness.

Scene 3

The WOMEN move around in single file until they form a semi-circle in front of the GODDESS who now stands in the centre of the performance area. She touches them softly on their heads with her huge, woody hands and they kneel down singing *'Om'*. They then touch their faces to the ground all together, stand up slowly and leave. Peace, harmony and warmth colour these first scenes.

Scene 4

The trees and the women are gone. There is nothing happening. The violin plays staccato and with a huge grunt the first GREY MAN jumps out, preferably from behind a building, if there is one in your performance area. He walks and creeps around belligerently and is joined by three more of his kind who appear simultaneously a few minutes later. They join forces and decide on a plan of action.

Scene 5

The MEN call out THE CITY. It comes out in groups of two or three tower blocks, jerkily, sometimes unwillingly. At last all six blocks are out and form a disordered city. The men admire their buildings, play with them, stroke them, fight over them.

They decide to build specific cities – calling out the names of *'Tokyo'*, *'New York'*, *'London'*, whereupon after each name the CITY is herded into one area and then another, all blocks moving together to re-form into different city shapes. At last the MEN, tiring of their game tell the CITY to go back and all the blocks retreat to be left standing against a bench or a handy wall.

Scene 6

The GREY MEN get more and more excited, they start moving in unison and shouting in a crescendo *'Monster, Monster,*

Monster . . .' And finally in comes a squat, grey being on wheels with three arms holding instruments of destruction (e.g. axe, chainsaw, dynamite). It comes in fast with bulging eyes and a red, protruding mouth and attacks two TREES that are once more standing nearby. As the second one is felled the WOMEN are hovering frantically on the outskirts. They feel helpless but still, in anger, they advance on the MONSTER and face the audience. The stage is theirs for a moment, the GREY MEN and the MONSTER are stilled and they watch while the WOMEN sing their dirge.

The dead men rise and open their eyes
Ready to buy and sell
To cut down trees
And melt their steel
For Nestlé, Rolls-Royce and Shell
They live and die
For ICI
And from safe behind their wall
They buy and they sell
A vision of hell
A curse upon them all.

And you who start
And create with your hands
The gallows, the bombs, the guns
Who drop your pence in the Oxfam box
After the killing is done
And draw your pay
And turn away
From the ones up against the wall
Go to your bed and sleep like the dead
A curse upon you all.

The tears run down
Through city and town
Like rain the tears do fall

The dead men stand
With blood on their hands
But blood is upon us all
The world may die
Before our eyes
And we weave her shroud and fall
Write on her tomb
We are your doom
*A curse upon us all.**

Scene 7

The WOMEN turn to the GODDESS who embraces them as a group. Then she shows them what to do. She moves slowly with stately dignity to a TREE (at least two more TREES stand in the performance area) and she embraces the TREE. She moves to the next one and does the same – looking at the women as if to say 'This is how you can protect yourselves.'

Afterwards she moves back to the side and leaves the WOMEN to take action. Two WOMEN at each TREE. They hold arms in front of the TREES and turn their faces to the oncoming MONSTER.

Scene 8

The MONSTER and the GREY MEN need more trees and they once again attack with fury, but this time their weapons can't reach the TREES – the WOMEN's bodies protect them. As they vainly try the second TREE, the WOMEN and the GODDESS group together and chant three times *'It is necessary that we do what we must do.'* They continue the chant as on line 1 of *'Do'* with the men chanting as on line 2 (see below).

*Adapted from Peggy Seeger

With the final three 'do's' the WOMEN push the MONSTER and the GREY MEN off the performance area and shout among themselves and to the audience, *'Do, do, do . . .'* as they also leave, emphasizing the necessity of action.

DO

1 It is necessary that we do what we must
2 *It is*

1 do. To do less
2 *necessary that we do*

1 is to fail. To fail
2 *what we must do.*

1 is to suffer and in this
2 *To do less is to fail.*

1 so short, so fragile existence
2 *To fail is to suffer*

1 we must do what we must.
2 *and in this so short,*

1 It is necessary, so necessary
2 *so fragile existence*

1 that we do
2 *we must do what we must.*

1 what we must do. And this is said
2 *It is necessary,*

1 with the certainty
2 *so necessary that we do*

1 that what we must do we can do.
2 *what we must do.*

1 To fail in doing what we must
2 *And this is said*

1 is to fail
2 *with the certainty* *that what we must do*

1 in this life and this life is all
2 *we can do.* *To fail*

1 that we have. Nothing more
2 *in doing* *what we must*

1 is given. So we can do no less
2 *is to fail* *in this life*

1 than to do what we must
2 *and this life* *is all*

1 and we must do
2 *that we have.* *Nothing more*

1 what we must do.
2 *is given.* *So we can do no less*

1 do do do
2 *than what we must* *and we must*

1 do.
2 *what we must.*

Scene 9

The MUSICIANS play while the players run to become BIRDS. (We had three birds, each needing three people to support it. They should come from far away so the audience sees them coming nearer and, in true Bread and Puppet tradition, should circle the burning evil figure. We did not burn our MONSTER, firstly because it took so long to build and we wanted to act our theatre several times and, secondly, because this evil figure is still lurking. So our BIRDS only circled the performance area, once, twice and left. This is a mystical scene.)

Scene 10

All the PLAYERS slowly come back to form a semi-circle in front of the MUSICIANS who have played all through the arrival and departure of the BIRDS. The PLAYERS pick up the music and sing their final song *'I am an Old Lady'*.

I am an old lady
What can I say?
It's just like my young and old sisters all say
Our jungle's for timber and grass
These trees are our hearts
These trees are our lives
One who will fell them will also cut us
Will saw us instead of trees
*That's all.**

*Words of a Chipko woman

JOINT SECOND PRIZE 15 AND OVER

THE TALE OF MIGHTY HAWK AND MAGIC FISH

by Jo Dorras and Peter Walker
for Wan Smolbag Theatre

PORT VILA, VANUATU,
SOUTH WEST PACIFIC

AUTHORS' NOTE

We hope that in some sense this is a myth for modern times. The hawk was an important symbol in traditional Melanesian culture. It symbolised the ultimate state of freedom to which men aspired in their progression through the grades or ranks of their society. Relationships between birds and fish was also a common feature of their myths and legends.

Mighty Hawk and Magic Fish was first performed by Wan Smolbag (One Small Bag) Theatre in Vanuatu in the South Pacific. The group tries to make plays simply with anything that can be carried in one suitcase – although it is sometimes hard to shut the lid!

We travel around the many islands that make up Vanuatu, presenting plays with strong health and environmental messages. By showing that theatre can be made with a minimum of props, we hope to encourage people in villages to use the minimum themselves.

For *Mighty Hawk and Magic Fish*, the main props were a single chair and a wooden chainsaw that we made. When Mighty Hawk was flying, she stood on the chair and, using her hands as claws, grabbed Magic Fish by the shoulders. They stayed on the spot, swaying to suggest a flying motion.

The Fish and the Hawk wore bright clothes and ornate masks – although strictly speaking these were 'hats', so as not to hide their faces or make them difficult to hear. Cola was played by an actor in a cardboard box covered with rubbish.

The actors should be prepared to ad lib when interacting with the audience. A good Kill the World can whip up the audience in true panto fashion.

All the parts can be played by men or women, although there are no female chiefs in Vanuatu!

Characters

MIGHTY HAWK (Bird)
MAGIC FISH
MR KILL THE WORLD (KTW)
COLA, A ROBOT MADE OF RUBBISH
THE CHIEF

On one side of the stage a fish swimming. On the other a bird flying.

BIRD: (*Singing*)

When I am hungry
I fly across the sea
Looking for a nice fat fish
To take home for my tea!

FISH: (*Also singing*)

Today, Today,
I'll have my swim today,
Twist and turn,
Up and down, in and out . . .

BIRD: There! A tasty looking fish . . .

FISH: Through the lovely coral . . . What's that shadow?

BIRD: Just what I wanted.

FISH: Perhaps he hasn't seen me . . . Just keep swimming.

BIRD: Slow down . . . hover . . .

FISH: Pretend nothing has happened . . .

BIRD: Down I go . . .

FISH: I know, sing a song . . . act normally . . . (*Singing*.)

Today, today . . .

BIRD: Down and down . . .

FISH: I'll have my swim . . .

BIRD: And attack!

FISH: Ooh! Aah! Put me down . . . I'm frightened.

BIRD: Yes, I'm going to put you down . . .

FISH: Yes, yes please now . . .

BIRD: Down my throat.

FISH: Oh no, have mercy . . . please. I'm a good fish . . . I go to fish church on Sundays . . . I've a fish wife and six fish children.

BIRD: I have children too . . . at home and they're hungry . . . they're waiting for their supper.

FISH: What are they going to eat?

BIRD: You!

FISH: Me? But I don't taste nice. I'm all bone. Look at me.

BIRD: You're fat enough.

FISH: Oh, well, if you really think so . . . (*They fly along*.) Nice view from up here. You birds are lucky . . . I can see so much . . . look at the village . . . and the forest.

BIRD: That's where we're going. They're waiting for you.

FISH: Oh let's not talk about that now . . . let me enjoy my last five minutes. I like flying, Bird, I should have been a flying fish. Ha! Ha! Ha! Wee! This is fun. (*Shouting*.) Hello down there, hello. Look at all those children. Hello, children! Wee! C'mon Bird. Faster.

BIRD: You're very happy.

FISH: Yes, aren't I? Hello . . .

BIRD: You should be dead.

FISH: What?

BIRD: Fish can't breathe out of water.

FISH: I can.

BIRD: How?

FISH: I'm not telling you.

BIRD: C'mon, fish, I'm the Great Hawk of the Skies (*Gives a shake*.) Now tell me . . .

FISH: Nope, shan't.

BIRD: I order you!

FISH: You're going to eat me anyway, so you can shake me as much as you like . . . but I'm not going to tell you (*Pause – they fly along*, FISH *sings*.)

BIRD: Perhaps I won't eat you.

FISH: (*Singing*) I'm so happy – I'm a bird today!

BIRD: Did you hear what I said?

FISH: You said you wouldn't eat me.

BIRD: Aren't you pleased?

FISH: How do I know it's true?

BIRD: You'll have to trust me.

FISH: Well, start flying back to sea. Then I might believe you.

(BIRD *turns sharply, fish is very shocked.*) Did you have to turn so suddenly? You've made me feel quite sick.

BIRD: Now tell me. How do you breathe out of water?

FISH: I'm a magic fish.

BIRD: A magic fish? (BIRD *turns back.*) I've never heard such nonsense.

FISH: Wait . . . wait . . . it's the truth . . .

BIRD: You see that big rock down there? I'm going to drop you right on it. It won't hurt you if you're magic, will it?

FISH: No wait, stop, please. I'm not as magic as that.

BIRD: Aha! So what can you do?

FISH: I can breathe out of water.

BIRD: Yes, but what else? What use are you?

FISH: I can tell the future.

BIRD: Ha! I don't need to tell the future.

FISH: But you do, you do. There are bad things coming to your forest.

BIRD: Bad things?

FISH: Yes, and bad things to my sea too.

BIRD: What bad things?

FISH: Human beings. Man. They don't like the sea and the forests. They want to hurt us.

BIRD: You sound just like the old tree in our forest.

FISH: You mean old Tatu the Fig tree?

BIRD: You know him? How do you know?

FISH: We're . . . we're old friends.

BIRD: You're a very strange fish . . .

FISH: Well?

BIRD: Well what?

FISH: Are you going to let me live?

BIRD: When will these bad things happen?

FISH: Soon.

BIRD: How soon?

FISH: Thirty seconds.

BIRD: What?

FISH: In thirty seconds – twenty-five seconds now. A big man in a big black car will drive into your village and ask them to let him cut down your forest.

BIRD: I don't believe it!

FISH: Look, down there, on the road. What's that?

BIRD: (*Without thinking*) a big black car, why? A BIG BLACK CAR?!? But, but Fish, they wouldn't . . . they couldn't, why do they want to cut down my forest? . . . my forest . . .

FISH: They're always cutting things down, moving earth . . . changing things.

BIRD: But where will we live? What will happen to all my Aunties and Uncles and Brothers and Sisters?

FISH: Hah! They don't care about them! . . . Hey, what are you doing? You promised to take me home!

BIRD: I haven't got time now. I must fly back. Warn everyone . . .

FISH: What about me?

BIRD: All right, all right. But I can't take you all the way back. I'll drop you down there and you swim home, OK?

FISH: It's 33 km and there's a lot of sharks.

BIRD: I'm sorry, Fish, but I can't stop. (*Releases* FISH.)

FISH: (*Falling*) Waa! You ungrateful . . . you horrible hawk . . . just you wait . . . you'll be sorry. You'll need my help again . . . but I won't be there . . . but I won't be there . . . because I'll have been eaten by a shark! Thanks to you . . .

BIRD: (*Swooping down*) All right! I'll take you home . . . (*They fly*.)

FISH: I knew you were a good bird really.

BIRD: What can we do, Fish? How can we stop them cutting down our forests?

FISH: Talk to the children in the village.

BIRD: Uh?

FISH: Get them to help you.

BIRD: How can they help?

FISH: Well, Mr Kill The World . . .

BIRD: Who?

FISH: Mr Kill The World . . . he's the man in the black car. He knows that if he can get the children to like him, then they'll tell their parents what a nice, good man he is.

BIRD: So I must warn the children.

FISH: That's right.

BIRD: But they'll never listen to me.

FISH: Why not?

BIRD: He'll offer them sweets and nice things.

FISH: So?

BIRD: Children love sweets and when Mr Kill The World says 'Have a sweetie, little one,' they'll gobble them all up and then Mr Kill The World will come and cut down our lovely forest . . .

FISH: You don't know children. They don't care about sweeties – they like places to play and the open air. They like trees to climb and they like to pick fruits in the forest.

BIRD: Ahh . . . and they like to shoot their catapults at the birds.

FISH: That's only the naughty ones.

BIRD: If you know all about children, come and talk to them.

FISH: What?

BIRD: Come with me now to the village and talk to the children.

FISH: But what about my wife? She was preparing a nice seaweed soup for supper . . .

BIRD: What about my family and me? Do you want Kill The World to destroy us?

FISH: Mmm . . .

BIRD: Fish, it is not often that the Mighty Hawk begs.

FISH: Oh all right.

KTW: Freeze! (BIRD *and* FISH *turn to stone.*) You look, what did I tell you? My magic spell works brilliantly . . . so now I can reach the children before them and soon all this forest will be mine. Haa! Haa! Haa! Children, children. How nice to meet you. Do you know my name? What is

it then? I can't hear you. Hey, Cola . . . They don't know me. I'm Mr Kill The World. Say it, children, say it . . . That's better! Yes, Kill The World's my name and I have come with my dear friend, Cola here, to speak to you all. Cola, where are you, you idiot. Cola!
(*Composite rubbish creature arranged round packs of Cola, emerges.*)
Now, he may look a little strange, but he's very useful, very friendly. He can do wonderful things. Just wait and see . . .

Now children, I have come to talk to you. As you see, I'm a big man. (*Pushing out stomach.*) What am I? Yes, a big man, and I've got a big black car, what have I got? Yes, a big black car. But I want more. What do I want? Yes, I want more. And how am I going to get it? Well, children, here you can help me and I can help you. Look children, all around this village are trees. Old trees, trees that have been here for years. They're not doing anything. They're no good to you. But if you let me have them I can turn them into money. All the money you want.
(COLA *becomes excited.* KTW *has to 'turn him down'.*)
It won't take long, a couple of weeks to cut down the forest, a short time to sell the wood, then I will bring all the money back to you, keeping just a little for myself. Think of all the sweeties, children, think of the Coca-Cola. If you give me the trees, you can have everything you like. Think of it, children, think of it!

BIRD: Don't let him have the trees, children, don't . . .

KTW: You! What happened to my magic? Must have worn off! Cola!
(*All sorts of rubbish is thrown by* COLA *– but* BIRD *keeps on, fights off* COLA.)

BIRD: Children, think of our wonderful forest. The creatures that live in it. The green leaves. The sun can't find you in the forest. And if you cut it down, what will be left? Children!

KTW: Shut up, stupid bird. You can't win. The children might listen to you, but the elders won't. They know all about money. You need money for school fees. And I can give them money! Lots of lovely money! You'll see, bird. Come on, Cola, we'll find the elders and the chief! Ha Ha Ha!

(*They exit.*)

BIRD: Fish! Fish! Oh, no, it must be the magic. Children: if you shout, 'Wake up, Fish!' I'm sure he'll wake up. All together now: 'FISH WAKE UP.' Fish, we must talk to the children. Kill The World's off to see The Chief.

FISH: (*To the Children.*) Let me teach you a song about the trees. It will help you to understand why we must save the forest. And you can sing it to other children. Bird, hold up the words for the children.

BIRD: I gave them to you, Fish.

FISH: Are you sure?

BIRD: I tell you, you've got them, you stupid fish.

FISH: Oh dear, oh yes, yes you're right. Would you please help me hold them up for the children to see, Bird? Thank you so much.

BIRD and FISH: Trees are everywhere
They give us many things
A home for many creatures
And many medicines
But people want to cut them
Clear the forest away
And if we cut them down
We'll get some money quickly
But in the end we'll pay,
Yes, in the end we'll pay.

BIRD: All right, children, you see why it's so important?

FISH: C'mon, Bird, I must go home, my wife will be worried.

BIRD: Yes, but first we must explain to the children. Now, listen, children, you've a very important job. You have to save the forest.

FISH: Mr Kill The World is going to try and force the Chief to let him cut the forest. You must warn the Chief . . .

BIRD: Every time Mr Kill The World speaks, you say 'Don't listen to him.'

FISH: But the Chief won't take orders from children.

BIRD: You're right. I've an idea. The children must pretend to be the wind. The wind shall speak to The Chief. You whisper, children. Do you understand? Let's try it. (*Practice follows until Children have got it right*)

BIRD: That's it. Well done, OK. Fish, let's go. Remember, children, only you can save the forest.
(*They take off.*)

FISH: Ow! Oo! Careful! Bird. Watch those claws, you're hurting me.

BIRD: Shut up or else I'll feed you to the sharks.

FISH: I don't know why I help a rude bird like you. Ah Oo!
(*Exit.*
Enter MR KILL THE WORLD *and the* CHIEF)

CHIEF: Explain to me again; what is it you want?

KTW: If you let me cut down the trees . . .

CHIEF: Did you hear something?

KTW: No, sir.

CHIEF: I thought I heard someone speaking . . .

KTW: No, no there's no one here. As I was saying, if you let me cut your forest down, I will make you a rich man . . .

CHIEF: It's funny, I'm sure I can hear voices.

KTW: Nonsense!

CHIEF: Is that how you speak to a chief?

KTW: I'm sorry, sir, you're quite right. Yes, yes I can hear voices . . . in the wind: They're saying, 'Listen to him, listen to him.'

CHIEF: No, they're not. They're saying, 'Don't listen to him. Don't listen to him.'

KTW: Oh honestly, sir, why should the wind say that, when I'm offering you all this money?

CHIEF: The forest gives us fruit, the dead wood gives us

fuel. There are many herbs, many medicines.

KTW: But with my money, you can buy all these things and more; radios, cars . . . your family will be rich . . .

CHIEF: (*Echoing Children's voices*) Don't listen to him . . . don't listen to him . . . (*Snaps out of trance.*) No Mr Kill The World. I'm sorry, I don't trust you. I will not let you cut down my forest. Goodbye.

(*Exit.*)

KTW: Oh children, you think you are so clever, pretending to be the wind . . . I can see that I shall have to try harder. The first job is to destroy that magic fish! Cola! . . . Cola! Come here . . .

(*Enter* COLA, *saw at ready.*)

KTW: No, Cola, no, the saw must wait. The Chief has listened to these foolish children , we cannot cut the forest. Yes, children, you can laugh now, but I shall win in the end, you'll see.

Now, Cola, let us search for the magic fish. If we can kill him, the bird can do nothing. My map of the ocean? Yes, about here, I should think. Cola, your oil pump, is it ready? Good. So here is the plan: you will row over the sea here . . . and pour thousands of litres of oil into the ocean. (*He smacks the map.*) All the fish in the area will die; they will float to the surface, eyes popping out of their heads. Cola, we will call this plan, pollution plan. Do you know that word, children? Pollution? Cola knows that word, don't you Cola? It's his favourite word. But children, before you tell me I am wicked, you like pollution too. I've seen you throwing your sweet papers into the sea. Dropping your cans of drink in the road. Throwing paper airplanes, crisp packets . . . rubbish . . . everywhere. Yes . . . so don't tell me I'm a bad man! Come, Cola, to work!

(*They go off. Enter* BIRD.)

BIRD: Phew! That fish is heavy. Carrying him all that way. Now children, what happened while I was gone? Did you pretend to be the wind? You did? Well done. And what did the Chief say? Have you saved the forest? Marvellous! Well done! Thank you for saving my life. But where's Kill The World now? What's that? He's gone to kill the magic fish? Oh children, that's terrible. How? What's he going to do.

(*Children explain.*) I must fly to save him. Oh, children, could you be the wind again? This time I want you all to blow, blow as hard as you can, so that I fly faster and reach Magic Fish in time.

(*Exit.* KTW *re-enters.*)

KTW (*Singing*)

Oil, spoil, pump and spit.
Throw the rubbish into it.
Yucky mucky, vile black slime
Kill all the creatures in the sea,
Bring magic fish here
Dead, to me!

(*Wild laughter.*)

That's my little song. Do you like my little song? Would you like to learn it children? After me . . . Oil, spoil, pump and spit! . . . All together now!

BIRD: (*Entering*) No, children, don't. He wants to kill the magic fish . . . Oh, what am I going to do? If my wings touch that oil, I'll never be able to fly again . . .

KTW: Do you like that water, Bird? Isn't it a pretty colour? Would you like to take a bath, my friend?

BIRD: You're evil, Kill The World, but you won't win. (*To audience*) We're going to save the magic fish, aren't we, children?

KTW: You're too late. He's in there! You see all those fish floating to the surface? Wave goodbye to your little fish friend. And soon, Bird, you'll be waving goodbye to your forest. Now you've got no fish to eat, the Chief will have to sell the forest.

BIRD: You won't win. They'll find you. You can't just drop oil in the sea like that; you'll be put in prison.

KTW: They'll never find me. They'll think it's a ship; ships are always spilling oil into the sea . . . And the sea's so big . . . what does it matter? Come, Cola. Enough. A good day's work.

BIRD: Oh children . . . our magic fish gone. I'll never forget him. Even though he did complain a lot. Do you remember when I used to carry him, 'Oo Ow' all the time! And now he's gone forever.
What a horrible man that Mr Kill The World is. Why do men want to spoil the sea and cut down the forest? Do you like the forests? Do you like the sea and the lakes, children? I'd like you to make me a promise. To show how much you liked Magic Fish, will you promise never to throw anything horrible into the sea again? Will you promise me that? I'm so sad. Perhaps we ought to sing a song together. Would you like that?

Song

Magic fish, magic fish
We'll never forget you
We promise now to keep the sea
Clean for you
No plastic bags, no sweet papers
No styrofoam, no Coca-Cola tins.
We promise to keep the Sea
Clean for you.

FISH: (*From audience*) Hello, Bird, that's a very good song you're teaching the children.

BIRD: Magic Fish, you're alive!

FISH: Yes, of course I am.

BIRD: But the oil . . .

FISH: What oil?

BIRD: Over there . . . you're swimming towards it, stop! Children, tell him to stop . . .

FISH: What are you talking about? There's no oil.

BIRD: There is! Stop! Stop! Kill The World came here with

Cola and they poured oil into the sea. They wanted to kill you. They said you were helping me to save the forest . . .

FISH: But my baby fishes, they were all at home . . . my wife and I went to visit my brother. I must go and save . . .

BIRD: No, Magic Fish, it's too late. Believe me. I can see from up here, there are so many fish floating on the surface. You will die if you swim in there. I'm sorry, it's terrible about your children. But you must swim away . . . to a new home . . .

FISH: I knew something bad would happen today. Pick me up.

BIRD: What?

FISH: Take me up into the sky. I want a last look at all my children and my home . . .

(BIRD *picks him up.*) That was my home, Bird. All the coral we feed on destroyed. For ever. Oh well, at least we saved your home, Bird.

BIRD: I'm not so sure.

FISH: Uh?

BIRD: Mr Kill The World says that now all the fish are dead, the Chief will have to let him cut down the forest so that people can buy food.

FISH: Yes . . . yes . . . I can see that happening . . . Oh, Bird . . . hold me tight . . .

(*He starts shaking.*)

BIRD: What is it, Magic Fish, what's happening?

FISH: I'm having one of my dreams.

BIRD: Dreams?

FISH: When I see the future . . .

BIRD: What can you see, Fish?

FISH: I can see men with saws . . . and big trucks and . . .

BIRD: That's the forest . . .

FISH: And trees falling . . .

BIRD: Oh no . . .

FISH: Wait . . . I can see children. Now I can see . . .

BIRD: Yes?

FISH: It's not clear . . . it's not clear. Now I see a net . . .

BIRD: In the forest?

FISH: No, in the sea, a big net . . . stretching for many kilometres.

BIRD: Yes?

FISH: And I'm swimming . . . no, no, don't please . . . closer . . . swimming no . . . closer, I can't, I don't want . . . please . . .

BIRD: Fish, Fish are you all right?

FISH: Where am I?

BIRD: You were having dreams. You said there were saws in the forest . . . and children. Then you were swimming in the sea and there was a net.

FISH: That's right.

BIRD: What does it all mean, Fish?

FISH: I don't know . . . but I'm frightened, I am very frightened.

BIRD: Come with me. Back to the forest, for a while, until you feel stronger.

FISH: Yes, I'd like that.

(*They fly, freeze in flying position to indicate passage of time, then fly again.*)

BIRD: OK, down we go . . .

FISH: Whoa! I feel sick.

BIRD: You're a terrible flyer.

FISH: I'm better at flying than you are at swimming.

BIRD: That's true. Look, see that tree? It's two hundred years old.

FISH: Never!

BIRD: And that one. That's his daughter. She's a hundred and fifty!

FISH: Amazing.

BIRD: And, over there, that's his grand-daughter. She's only eighty years old. And that's my favourite tree. It's where we're going now.

FISH: Bird, one problem. How am I going to sit in a tree?

BIRD: I'll show you, down we go. I'm just going to drop you between those three branches there. One for your head, one under your tummy and one under your tail. (*He drops the Magic Fish.*)

FISH: Aah!

BIRD: All right?

FISH: I've broken every bone in my body.

BIRD: Sorry, it was quite a bump. Oh, Fish, I am tired . . . I'm just going to curl up here . . . and go to sleep; you should sleep too. We've a lot of work tomorrow.

FISH: I don't think I can sleep. I keep thinking of all my children.

BIRD: I'm sorry, Fish. It must be hard. I'll sing a little lullaby. Children, will you help me? I'll sing it first.

Fish and man and bird
Sea, earth and tree
I can't live without you
You can't live without me.

BIRD: Night-night, Fish.

FISH: Night-night, Bird.

(*They sleep.*)

BIRD: Fish, wake up! Wake up, Fish!

FISH: What is it? I was just having a wonderful dream, all about . . . Ahh . . .

BIRD: What's wrong?

FISH: I'm going to fall, Bird. It's so far down. Help! Help!

BIRD: You've been up here all night, you stupid fish. If you stay still, you won't fall.

FISH: I can't stay still, I'm shaking with fear. I've got vertigo.

BIRD: Far to go?

FISH: No! Vertigo, V-E-R-T-I-G-O.

BIRD: What's that? Is it a terrible disease?

FISH: No, well, not really. I'm afraid of being up high, far away from the ground. That's what vertigo means.

BIRD: Afraid of being high off the ground? What are you, a fish or a mouse?

FISH: A fish, of course.

BIRD: Well, fish swim on top of the sea, if you look down to the bottom, you don't get vertigo.

FISH: Because it's not far to go to the bottom.

BIRD: Stop it, Fish. We've got work to do this morning.

FISH: Work?

BIRD: Yes, Kill The World and Cola have just driven up to the village. Kill The World has piles of boxes in his car and all the women have started cooking. He's got a plan. Some way to make the Chief give him the forest, we'd better fly down and see what's happening.

FISH: Come on, Bird – there's not a moment to lose . . . Ah . . .

BIRD: Fish, what are you doing?

FISH: I forgot I can't fly . . .

(*Exit.*

Enter KTW *and* CHIEF.)

KTW: As I was saying, Chief, I enjoyed visiting your beautiful village so much that I decided to come back. I've a little food and drink. I thought the women could cook and we'd have a little celebration.

CHIEF: We don't want to celebrate. Bad things have happened here.

KTW: Yes, yes, I heard. That terrible oil spill. The beach was ruined and the coral . . .

CHIEF: Was killed along with so many fish . . .

KTW: Terrible, terrible. And I thought a little celebration, I mean a party, would cheer people up . . .

CHIEF: That's very kind of you.

KTW: Ah the food is ready. And the drink. Cola! Bring the Chief a drink. And let there be music!! Chief, if you will allow me, I will sing you the song of Mr Kill The World. And while I sing, eat, drink and be happy.

(*Sings*)

Birds and trees are very nice, I agree
And to watch the golden sun

Go down upon the sea
Is a sight enjoyed by everyone.

And here in Vanuatu
The sea's a bright clear blue
I've seen the little children joining hands
As they laugh and play upon the sand.

There's a million different fishes
Swimming in the sea
Some with stripes, some with spikes
And all look happy as can be.

But I'm afraid, I must confess
What I really like the best
Is a lot more use to me and you
Here I believe it's called the dollar.

Money is what I like and what I want
That's why I cut down trees
Make them into chairs
Rip forests away, no one really cares!

Chief, before I end my song
Why don't we all sing along?
Just a simple little rhyme
Let's make sure we keep in time.

(KILL THE WORLD *and the* CHIEF *dance.*)
Kill The World's my name
Kill The World's my aim
I've got no fear, I've got no shame
cos the world was made for me!!
(*The last verse gets more and more frantic as it's repeated. The* CHIEF *is very drunk and is about to collapse. He falls into* KILL THE WORLD*'s arms, who produces a contract for the*

CHIEF *to sign.*)

KTW: (*Standing and looking at the drunken body of* CHIEF) So I have it. Look, Cola signed, signed. The rights to all the trees in the forest. Think what I could have got . . . All the land everything. Everything! Never mind, Cola, we'll start with the trees, OK? They're ours, ours, we'll cut them all down and sell the trees, sell them for lots of dollars. (*Laughing hysterically.*)

CHIEF: (*Rising to his feet and dancing in front of* COLA)
Mr Kill The World,
That's my name and my aim . . .
(CHIEF *turns to face* MR KILL THE WORLD, *who stares coldly at him.* CHIEF *stops dancing.*)

KTW: Cola, take this fool away and fetch the saw.
(COLA *carries* CHIEF *off. Returns with chain saw.*) What a beautiful saw. Look how it shines. How easily it will slice through those old trees. It will cut down one after the other, bam, bam until there are no trees left, no trees left.

BIRD: You can't do it, Kill The World. (*Flying in.*)

KTW: I've done it, my friend, I've done it and there's nothing that can stop me now!

BIRD: But why, why destroy the forest? It's beautiful. It's my home.

KTW: I need money, Bird. I need a newer, faster car, a louder stereo, a bigger house.

BIRD: But without the forests the world can't survive!

KTW: Rubbish, Bird, rubbish. Stop this foolish talk, you can't change me.

FISH: Kill The World, listen to me, I can see things you cannot. If you continue, if you cut and chop away at the trees, a terrible end will come to you. I can see it. The air will become poison, it will choke you and the seas will rise up and drown you, drown all the land . . .

KTW: (*Hands over ears*) No, no, Fish, you're just trying to frighten me. But you can't frighten Kill The World. (*Pushing them aside.*) Out of my way, you'll have to do

better than that if you want to save the forest.
(*Exits.*)

BIRD: Cola! Cola! Don't follow him, please don't cut down my home. Have you no heart, Cola? Listen, I have children in the forest and many friends. They live in the trees' branches, or dig beneath the trees' roots. It's not just the forest you destroy, but them too. Please listen, Cola. Don't help Kill The World . . .
(COLA *remains still.*)

FISH: You won't get to him, Bird. Look he's made of plastic and rubbish. He doesn't understand life or beauty. Like you said, he has no heart.

BIRD: But every living creature has a heart.

FISH: Cola isn't a living creature. He's Kill The World's toy. Kill The World made him out of every piece of rubbish he could find. Rubbish, that's what Cola is, just rubbish. (COLA *begins to cry softly.*) But even some of that rubbish comes from the earth and maybe somewhere deep inside himself, Cola loves the trees.

BIRD: Please Cola . . . children, I think Cola might join us. Help me, help me change his mind.

KTW: Come on, Cola, it's time to start.

BIRD: Call out, children, call out 'DON'T DO IT COLA.' Come on!

KTW: (*From off*) Cola, Cola, where are you?

BIRD: Come on children: 'Don't do it Cola, don't do it Cola'.

KTW: You stupid machine, I'll tear you to pieces when I find you!

BIRD: Children, keep shouting. 'Don't do it Cola.'

KTW: Cola, if you aren't here in one minute I'll . . .
(*Children shout,* COLA *moves slowly and sadly away.*)

BIRD: Oh Fish, we've failed. Children, it's terrible, terrible.

FISH: Don't worry, Bird, you nearly got Cola to join us. Next time you may even succeed. (*Sound of chain saw.*)

BIRD: What's that noise?

FISH: I don't know. It's frightening.

BIRD: It's getting louder.

FISH: And louder.

BIRD: Come on, Fish, let's get back to my tree. Quick . . .
(*They exit.*)

KTW: (*Entering.*) That's a beautiful sound, Cola, turn it on again. What do you think of that, children! Loud, isn't it? What is it? Yes, loud. Makes your teeth chatter doesn't it, children? It makes your teeth, what? Yes, chatter. What am I going to do with it? That's right I'm going to cut that bird's forest down, tree by tree . . . And if any naughty boys and girls try to stop me, I might just give them a hair cut they won't like.
(*Brandishes chain saw over their heads.*)
Do you understand, boys and girls? My advice to you is sit quietly like good little angels. Cola . . . What's that you're saying?

COLA: . . . (*A squeaking sound.*)

KTW: 'Where are the poor birdies going to live?' Cola, what are you talking about?

COLA: . . . (*Squeaking sounds.*)

KTW: 'All those pretty flowers will die?!!' Of course they will, Cola, I know that . . .

COLA: . . . (*More squeaking.*)

KTW: You feel sorry for them? Cola, what's happening to you? Pull yourself together. Remember, I've promised you new arms and legs when I've sold all this wood.
(COLA *does nothing.*)
Cola, Cola come over here . . . sit on my knee, come on. There's a good Cola. Now listen very carefully, Cola. I made you. Do you understand? I am your master. You do what I tell you. If you don't, I can take your arm off. (*Takes it off.*) I can take a leg off. (*Takes a leg off.*) And if I don't put them back on again, you are nothing, you are rubbish. Do you understand, Cola?
(COLA *nods.*)
Good. So pick up your saw and let's get to work.

(KILL THE WORLD *starts to go off,* COLA *turns and waves sadly to the Children.*)

C'mon, Cola.

(COLA *goes off.* MAGIC FISH *and* BIRD *in their tree. They are shaking. The forest echoes to the sound of timber falling.* BIRD *is looking out from the tree.*)

FISH: He's getting closer.

BIRD: I don't want to know. He's won. It's the end of my forest.

FISH: We can still try, Bird.

BIRD: How?

FISH: I don't know but . . .

BIRD: You're supposed to be a magic fish and you don't know what to do.

FISH: But my dream . . .

BIRD: Your dream, Ha! You saw the forest being chopped down in your dream.

FISH: That wasn't all I saw.

BIRD: It's no good, Magic Fish. Look, I'd better take you back to the sea.

FISH: No, I'm staying with you.

BIRD: No.

FISH: I am.

BIRD: No, Fish, the fight is over. I'm just going to lie down and let him chop me down. I'm not going to fly away. I've lived here too long. When the tree dies, I die.

FISH: That's stupid. Did I give up when all my children died? Did I go and swim into all that oil?

BIRD: That's different.

FISH: Why?

BIRD: It just is.

FISH: That's not a reason.

BIRD: Leave me alone. I've made up my mind.

FISH: So you're going to let man destroy the world? You're going to let Kill The World chop down this forest?

BIRD: Yes.

(BIRD *lies down.*)

FISH: Ha! The Great Hawk of the Skies! I used to be frightened of birds. Now I see birds are not as brave as fish, probably not as brave as an ant or gekkos! (*Pause.*) Come on Bird! What's wrong with you? The Great Hawk doesn't give in. The Great Hawk is Master of the Skies. He fights to the last feather!

(*Silence.*)

Bird, Bird, listen to me. If we don't fight now . . . it's happening . . . I can see it happening. I'm having a dream. They've chopped down all the trees. The Earth is brown and ugly, everywhere great factories are throwing smoke into the sky. I can't see the sun. Let me go to the sea, my sea, Oh it's filthy, Bird. So dirty. The coral's all dead. Fishes, where are you? No answer. Look at the plastic bags everywhere, the cans, the paper, rubbish, rubbish. Help me, Bird! Help, help me, Bird!

BIRD: So there's no hope. Better to die now, Fish. I'm getting weaker; soon my heart will stop and my soul will fly off to join the other hawks . . .

FISH: There was another part to the dream, Bird.

BIRD: I've heard enough.

FISH: It doesn't have to end that way. If we can win, Bird, the world will continue green and blue forever! Bird! Bird! We must fight Kill The World.

(*Silence.*)

It's hopeless, he won't listen. There must be a way to make him listen. Yes, of course! Children, children, help me! If we can make Bird remember all the good things. All the things he loved, perhaps he'll come back to life again. We must be quick though, children (*touching* BIRD'*s heart*), because he's almost dead.

FISH: Quickly, children, make the sound of the wind; more, more, I can feel a heart beat. It seems a little stronger. Now, yes, yes, the birds talking in the evening, make the sounds of the birds! A little stronger still. Come on , children, we'll save Bird yet! Now the sea, be the sea slapping against the rocks. Look look, his wings are moving. Come on, children. Wake up, Bird!

BIRD: It's morning in the forest. The forest is all here, it hasn't been chopped down.

FISH: What do you mean, Bird?

BIRD: Those beautiful sounds. The sounds of the forest.

FISH: No, Bird. That was the children. They didn't want you to die. They made the sounds to bring you back to life.

BIRD: Oh . . .

FISH: They want us to save the forest. They want to help us. Bird you're not going to disappoint them. Now we've got help.

BIRD: Help? You mean those little children. How can they help? Look at them. I could knock them down with one of my feathers. Haa! See I can destroy the lot of them! Fish! You interfering creature, why did you bring me back to life.

FISH: I've got a plan, Bird!

BIRD: A plan, what good is a plan against a chain saw? You're hopeless, I should have eaten you that first day. I should have swallowed you head first. In fact, I should do it right now!

FISH: You big bully. These children have worked to get you back to life; they love you. But you, all you care about is yourself, you don't even want to save the forest.
(*Silence*.)
What's the matter, Bird? You're crying. The Great Hawk is crying.

BIRD: Shut up, Fish.

FISH: Tell the children you're sorry.

BIRD: I'm sorry, children.

FISH: Do you want to hear my plan?

BIRD: All right.
(*They whisper together and run off*.)
BIRD *and* FISH *rush back to the stage, each carrying the rope,*

and pulling like mad. FISH *signals to* BIRD *to turn round and round therefore pulling the rope and also* COLA. *They finish up with* COLA *pulled into the acting area and really free, while they are both tied up in the rope.*)

FISH: Got you, Cola!

BIRD: It's hard to say who's got who.

FISH: Don't be silly, Bird. We've captured him and now we'll make him do whatever we like.

BIRD: That's wonderful, Fish. Except I can't move, can you?

FISH: (*Trying desperately to get free*)
Cola, you are our prisoner. We want you to understand that we will not hurt you . . .

BIRD: We won't even touch you. (*Showing that he can't move his arms.*)

FISH: Enough, Bird! All we want to do is show you the forest. Yes, show you the forest, you want to destroy. We know Mr Kill The World has no heart but we think you . . . you might have a heart. (COLA *begins to turn slowly round and round until he is tied up and the other two are free.*)

BIRD: I think he wants to be our prisoner!

FISH: Come on, children, let's show him the forest quickly. I think we can get Cola on our side. Then Mr Kill The World won't be able to cut down the forest!

BIRD: Curl up, children, as small as you can, into trees. Look Cola, here are all the tiny seeds, that will grow into trees. Now slowly, children, very slowly, reach up into tall young trees.

FISH: Do you know how many years it takes for those seeds to become trees, Cola? Forty, fifty, years Cola, nearly a lifetime. And these are young trees, Cola.

BIRD: Now, trees, breathe in, breathe out, breathe in, breathe out.

FISH: What are they doing, Cola? Do you know? They're giving us the air we breathe. They're making the air for us.

BIRD: Now sway in the breeze, trees.

FISH: See how beautiful they are, Cola? The wind blows through the trees, and the rain comes. The trees call the rain to water them. Call the rain, trees . . . softly call the rain.

BIRD: Without the trees, the rain won't come, Cola. Let's hear the sounds of the forest in the morning, children. Let's show Cola how the forest sounds as it wakes up . . . do you want to hear Cola? All the wonderful sounds, the birds, the insects, the wind, the sea.

BIRD: Now bring in the sound of the saw, Fish, take your saw and cut down the trees. Look, Cola, look at the young trees dropping dead. The birds and insects are flying away. They have no home, even the soil, the earth, is washing away into the sea.

FISH: Yes, the trees hold down the soil and when it rains now, the soil will wash on to the reef and kill the corals and the fish . . . (*Crying.*)

BIRD: Don't cry, Fish. Perhaps we can save the forest. Perhaps they won't cut it down.

FISH: No! No one cares. They just want to cut, cut, destroy, destroy . . . (*Sobbing . . . Sobbing grows louder and louder. Both* BIRD *and* COLA *join loudly.*)

BIRD: (*Drying his eyes*) Can you two stop that dreadful noise.

FISH: It wasn't just us. You were crying too!

BIRD: Us?

FISH: Yes, us.

BIRD: Don't you see, Fish?

FISH: See what?

BIRD: Look at Cola, can't you hear that terrible noise he's making?

FISH: Yes. (*Putting fingers in ears.*)

BIRD: Well, that means he cares about the forest.

FISH: Oh, I see. Cola, Cola shut up!

BIRD: That's enough, Cola!

FISH: (*Fingers still in ears*) How can we stop him? It's dreadful.

KTW: (*From off*) Cola . . . Cola.

BIRD: What was that?

FISH: Sounds like Kill The World.

BIRD and FISH: KILL THE WORLD?!?

(COLA *stops crying*.)

KTW: (*Entering*) Cola. There you are. What's happened? Have they taken you prisoner? Oh my poor Cola.

FISH: No, Kill The World, he tied himself up.

KTW: What?

FISH: He wants to stay with us. He knows that it's wrong to cut down the forest. He's our friend now.

KTW: But he's my slave. He stays with me and he cuts down your forest.

FISH: No, Kill The World. He's staying with us.

KTW: Oh no, he's not.

BIRD: Oh yes, he is.

KTW: Oh no he's not.

(*Grabs rope to pull* COLA *off*.)

BIRD: Come on, children. Help us pull hard.

(*A tug of war follows.* BIRD, FISH *and Children hold on to* COLA. KILL THE WORLD *pulls the end of the rope. Finally,* KILL THE WORLD *falls over and loses the tug of war*.)

FISH: Admit it, Kill The World, you're beaten.

BIRD: You thought you could destroy everything, well you were wrong!

FISH: Yes, Kill The World. Beaten by children, a bird and a fish. A big man like you beaten by a fish!

BIRD: Don't be so proud, little fish. It wasn't you alone.

FISH: But without me you'd have given up. Wouldn't you? Wouldn't you? I'm the greatest. The greatest fish alive. The Magic Fish, the brave fish; the great great great fish. Long live the Magic Fish. The greatest fish alive. I beat Kill The World; the greatest fish alive – Bum bum bum de bum.

KTW: We'll see, Fish (*Leaving acting area*.) We'll see.

BIRD: He's gone. What's that? Cola, still crying, when we've won? You're frightened? There's nothing to be frightened of now. Nothing.

(*Exit* COLA.)

FISH: Right, I'm off, I'm going back to the sea. Oh, I want a long wet bath. The sea, the sea, my home. C'mon, Bird.

(*They fly.*)

OK, Bird, you can drop me down here. It's been nice knowing you.

BIRD: Yes. You too. Look after yourself.

FISH: I will.

BIRD: Don't let the sharks get you.

FISH: I won't.

BIRD: I'll miss you.

FISH: I'll miss you. If you're in trouble again, just call.

BIRD: Yes.

FISH: Bye.

BIRD: Bye.

(BIRD *flies off.*)

FISH: Splash! Whoo! Back in the sea again! This is where I belong. Glomp! Mmm, delicious piece of algae. Glomp. Glomp. I haven't eaten for days.

(*Sings.*)

Today, today
I'll have my swim today
Twist and turn
Up and down, in and out.

(*Drift net suddenly traps* MAGIC FISH.)

What's happening? I can't move! I'm stuck. What is it? It's the net. The net I saw in my dreams.

(*Enter* KILL THE WORLD *in a swimming mask.*)

KTW: Yes, Magic Fish, it's a net, a drift net. You thought you'd beaten me when you captured Cola but I have other friends, fishermen friends. I asked for their help and they lent me one of their nets. The drift net. It catches everything that swims into it . . . and they stretch for 60, 70, 80 kilometres. They catch turtles, sharks, whales and, yes, they catch the Magic Fish! Try and escape, Magic Fish, if you like. Swim this way. Swim that way. Go on, try! You cannot get away. Oh Magic Fish, you made a big mistake.

FISH: Yes, I was too proud . . .

KTW: You were, you were . . .

FISH: I forgot the future, I forgot my dreams.

KTW: And now, you will die in a drift net. I am giving you to my fishing friends. There, they are pulling in the net. Bye! Bye! Magic Fish. You will make a very nice meal for someone, especially with some rice and vegetables. Ha! Ha! Perhaps we will meet again, Magic Fish . . . in heaven . . .

FISH: Heaven isn't for people like you, Kill The World. It's for good people . . .

KTW: Bye, bye, Magic Fish.

(MAGIC FISH *goes*.)

And now . . . back to the forest. I don't need Cola . . . I shall cut the trees myself!

(*Takes off mask and walks over to the other side of stage*.)

Yes, I'm going to cut down this horrible forest and I'll get lots and lots of lovely money for the trees. I'll have to give away a little bit of the lovely money to the stupid chief, but all the rest is mine, mine, mine! And with that money, you know what I'll do? I'll build a huge house, the biggest you have ever seen and all around it will be concrete – no earth, no flowers, no trees, just concrete everywhere, everywhere, until it covers the whole earth . . . where's my chain saw . . . now I'll begin!

(*Terrible sound of chain saw –* BIRD *flies in*.)

I'll start with that tree over there. Hear this tree? This is the end of you. (*Laughs madly*.)

BIRD: Kill The World! What are you doing? You're beaten! You can't come back here.

KTW: You don't know me, Bird. I'm never beaten. Ha Ha Ha!

BIRD: Cola, Magic Fish. Help! Kill The World's back.

KTW: Cola? He can't help you. He's just a stupid piece of plastic and as for Magic Fish, well you won't see him again.

BIRD: We beat you last time.
KTW: But this time Magic Fish is dead! Dead.
BIRD: Dead? No, I don't believe you. This is a trick. You want to frighten me, to make me leave the forest.
KTW: He's dead, Bird. Caught in the biggest net you've ever seen. (*Laughing*.)
BIRD: No! But I feel you are not lying. Kill The World, you are evil. Evil! How could you have killed him? The cleverest, best fish in all the world.
KTW: How? Simple. I made a net to cover the whole sea so that nothing could escape. Many, many creatures died with Magic Fish. Innocent whales and dolphins, quiet turtles and cruel sharks. But nobody, nothing can stop me. You try, Bird and see what happens.
BIRD: So you've won, Kill The World, with no Magic Fish to help me, I feel so weak. There's no point trying any more. It's over. Poor Magic Fish. I can't believe it. Cut down the forest, Kill The World, there's no one to stop you. Take all the trees. Kill the creatures that live in them. But one day, when it is too late, you'll realize . . . I'll hear the sound of the saw in a minute and the whole forest will be gone. My home, my family . . .
KTW: The sound of the saw, that wonderful sound. Hear it, Bird . . . (*Reaching for the saw, his hand is grasped from behind by* COLA)
AH! (*Looking round*.) Cola, So you have come to help me, now you see who is winning. I will be kind and take you back. Come, Cola, let go of my hand, there's work to be done. You're hurting my arm. Cola, Cola you heap of rubbish. Don't you know, I'm your master! You can't go against me. I control you, Cola. You see this remote control device? (*Taking device from pocket*.) If I press this switch here, you will die. Your motor will stop working forever!
BIRD: He means it, Cola. Let go or he'll kill you.
KTW: Did you hear Cola? Now, let go!

(COLA *does not let go and after a few seconds* KILL THE WORLD *presses the button and with a sad whirring noise* COLA *collapses, dead.* KILL THE WORLD *kicks the dead body.*)
Stupid lump of rubbish. That's the end of him. Now for the forest.
(*Exits.*)

BIRD: Children. I have been very weak. See how bravely Cola died? Well, let us be brave too. After all I'm the Great Hawk of the Skies. The others were only a fish and a pile of rubbish, but they didn't let Kill The World beat them. They fought him. Shall we fight him too? Shall we, children? Do you want Kill The World to chop down the forest? Do you? Shall we fight Kill The World? Well, come on children, what shall we do? No, no, no. We can't kill him. He's too strong for us. I know what we can do. We'll have to be very brave. Children, let's make a fence with our bodies between the trees and Kill The World. I don't think he can kill all of us. Can he? Let's do it, children.
(*Children come on to the acting area to make a fence. Re-enter* KILL THE WORLD.)
Now, Kill The World, kill all of us and get to the trees. Chop them down over our dead bodies!

KTW: Out of my way, damn you . . . Do you all want to die? Do you want me to kill you? Look little ones. I just want a few of those old trees . . . Out of my way. I said out of my way! Last chance, children. Hear the saw? Last chance.

BIRD: Be brave, children. Don't give in to him. Be brave.

KTW: Brave? It's stupid, stupid; out of my way!

BIRD: If you kill these children, Kill the World, you'll die too. Do you think their mothers and fathers will let you live? You'll die too.

KTW: Go away!
(*He starts the chain saw.*)

BIRD: No, we won't go away. You go away. Children tell him to go away.

(*Children shout at* KILL THE WORLD.)

KTW: Stop that terrible noise. You're breaking my eardrum.

BIRD: Now, be the wind, children and blow, blow him away.

KTW: No, no! Please stop, you're going to kill me! Aah no aah . . .

(KILL THE WORLD *is blown off the stage*.)

BIRD: Hooray, children! We've won. Now let's give ourselves three big cheers. Hip hip . . . hooray!

(*The rest of the cast appear for the final song*.)

Goodbye, goodbye, it's time to go,
We hope you have enjoyed yourself
Goodbye, goodbye we hope you know
The forest, the earth, the sea and the lakes,
Are good for you.
Goodbye, goodbye, please don't forget us
We'll come back again, if you let us!

THE END

SECOND PRIZE: UNDER 15

NATURE'S REVENGE

by Bhupesh Malhotra
(aged 14)

HELSINKI, FINLAND

Characters

NARRATOR (elderly male)
NATURE
MONKEYS
SCORPICON, *leader of the monkeys*
JANE
JOHN
GROUPS OF HUMANS
GROUP OF ANIMALS
BELIVION
THREE CHILDREN

NARRATOR'S VOICE: Children! Children, settle down and I will tell you a true story.

(*Small pause.*) Now then, listen carefully.

Once upon a time, not very long ago, Earth had almost been destroyed. It was now that Nature thought it was time to take its revenge. Nature, not being a person one could see, had a unique way of communicating with the animals. The animals couldn't see Nature, but they heard it.

One day Nature called upon all the animals to spread the word that a journey was to start . . .

(*During the last sentence the curtains rise. The view is stupendous and beautiful. Another voice starts.*)

NATURE'S VOICE: This journey is going to be our victory and revenge over savage humanity and all their followers. Even though in this journey we will not confront humanity, we will try to find people who support our victory. Through this journey we will gather humans who don't want to live in a world like this. As you all know, the world is now polluted and almost destroyed. The time has come to put my plans into effect, 'to fight evil with good'. This is why we have to make this journey around the world. I will assign separate groups to journey around separate parts of the world. Among these groups there will be one animal whom I will keep in touch with. I will guide you throughout this journey. Now go and await until tomorrow for my decision.

(*The animals go off the stage. As this is in the process the lights start to fade and the stage is dark again.*)

NARRATOR'S VOICE: The next day Nature contacted the animals whom it had chosen as its followers. These animals were all strong and fast, however, they were also wise and patient.

All the fish and water animals had been destroyed by humans. The rest of the species in the world, which were still alive, were told about this voyage. One animal from each strong species was chosen by Nature to guide the rest. The animals scattered all over the world where there were still admirers of Nature.

(*During the last sentence the lights start to come on very slowly. On stage are some* 'MONKEYS' *led by one* 'MONKEY'. *There is a row of houses on stage as well.*)

ALL THE MONKEYS: All people who help Nature in its revenge will be restored and not die, like those who oppose Nature. Nature has already thought of the fate of the savage humans and their treacherous followers. (*They are walking while they say this. Many* HUMANS *join the group of* MONKEYS *as they are walking. The leader of the monkeys,* SCORPICON, *is stopped at a house. The others stop as well. The two inhabitants of the house are outside.*)

JANE: Excuse me, sir. Please could you try to persuade my husband, John, that he should support Nature, like me, and not oppose it?

SCORPICON: I will try my best to persuade him. (*Going up to* JOHN.) Dear Friend, what your wife says is right, you should support Nature and oppose savage humanity and their followers.

JOHN: Why should I support Nature and not humanity, when humanity provides me with jobs, food and shelter?

SCORPICON: You are mistaken, my friend. It is not humanity who provides you with food and shelter, but it is Nature who gives you such things.

JOHN: I am indebted to humanity, who saved me from dying. I owe the race my life.

SCORPICON: It wasn't in your fate to die. Your destiny is to help Nature regain its old and forgotten beauty. Certainly, one of your age wouldn't know what Nature was like a few centuries ago. I myself don't know of Nature's beauty in those times, at least I haven't seen it. However, my mother told me about Nature. She told me what she had heard from her great-grandmother. She said that Nature had been a beauty, more beautiful than anything on earth today. She said it was always friendly with animals. However, it made the mistake of being friendly with man. Nature provided the animals with food and shelter, while man took these things from it. Nature thought that man would change himself, but man kept with his mischiefs. He quickly gathered followers, such as acids, chemicals and wastes. These followers polluted the Earth and destroyed the beauty of Nature while humanity sat with their luxuries, laughing. After all this you say that you are in debt of humanity, who saved maybe only one hundredth the amount of lives they destroyed.

JOHN: (*After a pause*) Maybe you are right. Maybe humanity did destroy Nature's beauty and almost destroyed Earth with it. But still, I am a human, and I will always stand on the side of humans until I obtain solid proof that tells me that the humans destroyed the Earth.

(JANE *exits the stage and* JOHN *sees her go*.)

Where are you going?

(JANE *returns after some time*.)

JANE: (*Coming onstage*) Look at this book, *The History of the Earth*. And look at this one: *Nature in the 20th Century*. (*Giving the books to* JOHN *one by one after calling the titles*.) Go ahead, read them and you will find from these old books that he is right (*pointing to* SCORPICON.)

JOHN: (*Skimming through the books, amazed*) In this book Nature is so beautiful. The plants, flowers, animals of all kinds big and small are everywhere. And now you don't see flowers very often. You only see them in wealthy people's houses. Same with plants. And the animals, they are almost extinct. Here it says that once there were thousands of horses and now there are only some hundreds left. What happened to these animals, how did they die?

SCORPICON: My dear friend, that is what I have been telling you. Humanity has destroyed the animals, flowers, and plants. Now the human race has come to the stage of destroying itself.

JOHN: Show me Nature and I will believe you.

SCORPICON: I have not seen Nature with my own eyes. However, all the animals have heard it. It is guiding us through this voyage. It has encouraged us not to lose hope, because it is going to be with us all the time. Why, Nature was guiding me through this very conversation. I was, at some moments, so angry that I could have killed you right then. But Nature was the one who was always calming me, and telling me to be patient.

JOHN: After this conversation, I am beginning to believe you. If you are right, then we must go and gather more people who support Nature, so they will not die because of the activities of the savage humans.

(*The group go offstage. The lights start to fade.*)

NARRATOR'S VOICE: As this conversation was taking place somewhere else other animals were gathering other people who supported Nature. At the end of a week they all met at the place where they started. Nature had told the guides of the groups to come to the starting place for a meeting. They were to bring the humans with them. On their way to the place, the humans saw the beauty of nature through their own eyes for the first time. This was the only part of Earth which had not yet been destroyed.

(*During the last sentence, the lights become brighter. We return to the place in the beginning of the story.* ANIMALS *enter the stage from both sides with the* HUMANS. *The* HUMANS, *startled, are looking around at the beauty of the place.*)

HUMAN NO. 1: What a beautiful place!

HUMAN NO. 2: I have never seen anything or any place like this.

NATURE'S VOICE: You have done your first task very well, children of Earth. Now I will give you your second and last task. This task will require wits and knowledge. Now you will have to confront the humans who are destroying the Earth and want to keep doing so. All you have to do is get rid of savage humanity. I will protect you and get rid of his followers. My human supporters will help you in your great voyage. Courage, my friends, courage is what you will need in this, your final voyage. And now, I bid you farewell and good luck. Remember, I will always be guiding you, through obstacles or war, I will always be with you.

(The ANIMALS *start exiting from one side of the stage. Some* ANIMALS *stay onstage.* SCORPICON *sees them, so he goes to a tree and faces the* ANIMALS *who are afraid.)*

SCORPICON: Dear friends, are you going to surrender before even starting the voyage? Are you going to fall without even resisting one obstacle? No, my friends, don't be so cowardly. Are you forgetting that Nature is guiding us this very moment? No, this is only our first test. The test of courage. There are many more tests to come through this journey. Just remember, that if we succeed in this voyage we will be returned to the beauty of Nature. Don't think you are fighting for someone else, think you are fighting for your own precious and beloved lives. Now friends come follow this road alongside me. This road will lead us to the beauty of Nature and the destruction of savage humanity. However, anywhere you go don't forget that 'Nature is with you wherever you are'.

(As the speech ends the ANIMALS *become more cheerful.* SCORPICON *finishes his speech and moves to exit the stage. All the* ANIMALS *follow him.)*

NARRATOR'S VOICE: All the animals, as Nature judged it,

had passed the first test. There were many other tests to come during the voyage of the animals. The next was the test of greed. The animals were in a desert caused by human activity. There was no water to be found and their food was also short. Scorpicon felt the beginning of another test. Scorpicon, a young and strong monkey, was among the wisest and surely the most patient of all the animals. All the animals depended on him for advice and encouragement. Scorpicon began thinking of how to overcome this test. One day while the animals were walking through the barren desert . . .

(*The lights become brighter and the audience sees a tree in the centre of the stage. The* ANIMALS *enter the stage.*)

HORSE: Look, a tree! We have very little food. Why don't we use this tree as a source of food.

(*Soon all the* ANIMALS *gather around the tree. The* ANIMALS *start arguing over whose tree it is.*)

HORSE: I saw the tree first so it is rightfully mine.

(*While the* HORSE *is saying this there are other* ANIMALS *shouting that the tree is theirs.* SCORPICON *enters. He goes straight to the tree and holds up his hands, signalling the* ANIMALS *for silence.*)

SCORPICON: Silence! Silence! Brothers, tell me, why do you argue over a tree.

ANIMAL: Because it is a source of food and we are in desperate need of food since our food is running out.

SCORPICON: It is true that we all need food now that our supply is coming to an end. But that is no reason to argue over a tree. We can all get the same amount of food by sharing. My friends, if we argue among ourselves some outsider will come and destroy us, if we don't destroy ourselves first. So don't be greedy and share with each other, that is the lesson that can be obtained by this test. Another lesson that can be obtained from this test is to unite yourselves. 'Unity is always strongest!' Now share the food from this tree among all the animals big or small.

(SCORPICON *takes a small branch from the tree. He goes around the group of animals, giving each* ANIMAL *one leaf from the branch. The leaves just never seemed to end. After this* SCORPICON *exits the stage. As soon as he goes out the animals joyously gather around the tree and happily start to share the food obtained from the tree.*

The lights start to dim as this ends.)

NARRATOR'S VOICE: Again Scorpicon had saved the animals from destruction. Now came the test of belief at the end of the five-month long journey. The animals were walking by a river . . .

(*The lights become bright again, we are now in the place described above. The* ANIMALS *enter the stage, not walking very quickly. As they are walking a machine appears in front of them. Later a man appears in front of the machine. He is* BELIVION.)

BELIVION: Stop there! I am Belivion. This is my loyal follower (*signalling to the machine behind him*). Before you pass this place you will have to answer my three questions. If you answer my questions correctly then I will have this machine destroy your enemies. But if you answer the questions incorrectly then I will have the machine destroy you.

ALL THE ANIMALS: What are these questions?

BELIVION: Very well, here is my first question: Who is the friend of all friends?

ALL THE ANIMALS: Nature, of course!

BELIVION: What is everyone's enemy?

(*There is a mumble in the group of* ANIMALS.)

SCORPICON: The worst enemy of all beings is not humanity (*facing the* ANIMALS), as many of you thought, but it is greed. If humans were not greedy the world wouldn't be this way.

BELIVION: What is the strongest of all powers?

ALL THE ANIMALS: (*In harmony*) Unity and harmony are the strongest powers of all.

BELIVION: You have answered all of my questions correctly. Tell me your enemy and it shall be destroyed immediately.

SCORPICON: Pardon us, sir, but we first have to complete our voyage before destroying our enemy ourselves. I am sorry we cannot ask your help since Nature has given us the task to destroy humanity. So if you kindly would let us pass and continue our journey.

(*The* MAN *and machine disappear. In their place appears a tree. This is* NATURE *itself.*)

NATURE: You have ended your journey, my friends. Yes, I am Nature. You have passed every test and obstacle and come to the end of your voyage. Scorpicon, come forwards and take a leaf from one of my branches.

(SCORPICON *obeys.*)

Now, take the leaf and place it on flat barren ground.

(SCORPICON *obeys while the* ANIMALS *wait in silence. Soon the leaf catches fire. One of the* ANIMALS *starts towards the leaf to stop the fire.*)

No, my friend, don't stop the fire. Let it burn!

(*The* ANIMALS *look in silence as the fire grows.*)

NARRATOR'S VOICE: This fire was not like normal fires. Instead of ash it left grass behind. For every human that died, a tree appeared. Soon the whole human race which opposed Nature had been destroyed.

NATURE: Let this be a lesson to all on the Earth. Whoever will try to destroy this beloved Earth shall perish under this fire. If you try to destroy me, this fire will destroy you first. Now, my friends, it is time for you to make a decision. Do you want to live in harmony or die in destruction like all of the human race who opposed the Earth. If you don't want this fate, then never destroy the Earth or take advantage of others' weaknesses. My friends, Let Earth prosper!

(*The tree disappears.*)

NATURE'S VOICE: Let Earth prosper! Let Earth prosper!

(*The lights fade. After some time the lights become brighter. We are now in a place with many trees. There are three* CHILDREN *sitting in front of an* OLD MAN *whose voice we have heard at the beginning of the play.*)

NARRATOR: Now you have learned the story of Nature's revenge. If you don't want the same fate as those who opposed Nature, never be greedy and always live in harmony with all other living things.

CHILDREN: Grandfather, how do you know that this story is true?

NARRATOR: I was afraid you would ask me that question. I will tell you what I have told no one. I must confess I have been trying to hide this. Do you remember the man John in the story?

(*The children nod.*)

Well, (*taking a deep breath*) I am that very person. Yes, I am John who first opposed Nature but after the voyage I have become a supporter of Nature.

(*Small pause.*)

Now, go and play with your animal friends, and don't forget the lessons you have learned from this true story.

(*The* CHILDREN *run off the stage leaving* JOHN *alone. The curtains close on the scene, slowly.*)

CHILDREN: (*In a song-like fashion, but not in unison*) Let Earth prosper, Let Earth prosper!

THE END

THIRD PRIZE: 15 AND OVER

CHILDREN OF THE RAINBOW

by André Surridge

HAMILTON,
NEW ZEALAND

AUTHOR'S NOTE

Children of the Rainbow is based on the North American Indian legend and prophecy about the Warriors of the Rainbow. It speaks of a time when peoples around the globe will unite and join forces in a struggle to protect the Earth. The story appeals to humanity's highest ideals, those of spiritual awareness and the sacredness of our planet.

This play is dedicated to all the peoples of the Earth and all the species of the Earth, past, present and future, and to the sacred Earth itself, our precious life-sustaining world.

The creation of this play would not have been possible without the assistance and inspiration of the following: Friends of the Earth, Chief Seattle, Greenpeace, Waikato Environment Centre, Royal Forest and Bird Protection Society, Arthur Hamilton, Cheryl Meier, Tim Surridge, Rae Somerville, The Sacred Earth Drama Trust.

Characters

THE SEVEN CHILDREN
OF THE RAINBOW

Red
Orange
Yellow
Green
Blue
Indigo
Violet

THREE BUSINESSMEN
(who represent the greedy
selfish interests of mankind)

WARRIOR OF THE RAINBOW

Lights up on a bare stage. Spotlights on a globe resembling the Earth and approximately two feet in diameter suspended about two feet from the ground. Incidental music, something mysterious. A mist swirls onstage. Enter the seven CHILDREN OF THE RAINBOW. *They are beautifully clothed, each in their respective colours,* RED, ORANGE, YELLOW, GREEN, BLUE, INDIGO *and* VIOLET. *They move towards the Earth in awe.*

RED: If the Earth were only a few feet in diameter, floating above a field somewhere, people would come from everywhere to marvel at it.

ORANGE: People would walk around it, marvelling at its big pools of water, its little pools and the water flowing between them.

YELLOW: People would marvel at the bumps on it and the holes in it and they would marvel at the very thin layer of gas surrounding it and the water suspended in the gas.

GREEN: The people would marvel at all the creatures walking around the surface of the ball and at the creatures in the water.

BLUE: The people would declare it as sacred because it was the only one and they would protect it so that it would not be hurt.

INDIGO: The ball would be the greatest wonder known and the people would come to pray to it, to be healed, to gain knowledge, to know beauty and to wonder how it could be.

VIOLET: People would love it and defend it with their lives because they would somehow know that their lives, their own roundness, could be nothing without it.

ALL: If the Earth were only a few feet in diameter.

(*Music. They dance. The dance is interrupted by a violent cacophany suggestive of heavy machinery in action, pneumatic drills etc; the* CHILDREN OF THE RAINBOW *scatter. Darkness. Lights up, different lighting. Enter the* BUSINESSMEN. *They approach the Earth. The cacophany recedes.*)

BUSINESSMAN 1: (*Rubbing his hands*) Exploitation!

BUSINESSMAN 2: (*Rubbing his hands*) Progress!

BUSINESSMAN 3: (*Rubbing his hands*) Civilization!

BUSINESSMAN 1: What we need is . . .

BUSINESSMAN 2: Oil!

ALL: Oil!

BUSINESSMAN 3: Gold!

ALL: Gold!

BUSINESSMAN 1: (*Pointing to the globe*) A canal here will save zillions of dollars.

BUSINESSMAN 2: Excellent.

BUSINESSMAN 3: Who needs this rain forest?

BUSINESSMAN 1: Not me.

BUSINESSMAN 2: There's plenty more.

BUSINESSMAN 3: Think what could be done with all that timber!

BUSINESSMAN 2: A huge dam here will create a megazump of hydro-electricity and satisfy the needs of a whole nation.

BUSINESSMAN 1: Power.

ALL: Power.

BUSINESSMAN 1: Nuclear power.

BUSINESSMAN 2: Even better! Our interests must be protected. (*Producing a plan.*) And here's a plan for fifty new nuclear power stations.

BUSINESSMAN 1: Wonderful!

BUSINESSMAN 3: Food?

BUSINESSMAN 1: I've just eaten, thanks!

BUSINESSMAN 3: (*Pointing to the globe*) No, food!

BUSINESSMAN 1 and 2: Ah food!

BUSINESSMAN 3: Clear this land, this land and this land, grow crops and feed the exploding population and make a few megatrillion dollars!

BUSINESSMAN 1: I like that!

BUSINESSMAN 2: Yes. Damn good idea.

BUSINESSMAN 1: Fishing!

BUSINESSMAN 2 and 3: Great!

BUSINESSMAN 1: Drift nets, high yield, maximum return on investment!

BUSINESSMAN 2: Amazing!

BUSINESSMAN 3: Wonderful!

(BUSINESSMEN *shake hands.* BUSINESSMAN 1 *hands out cigars.*)

BUSINESSMAN 3: (*Pointing to Antarctica*) What about this bit?

BUSINESSMAN 1: Antarctica!

BUSINESSMAN 2: (*Shaking his head*) Nothing much there except ice and penguins!

BUSINESSMAN 3: Minerals?

BUSINESSMAN 1 and 2: Minerals!

BUSINESSMAN 3: A little oil, perhaps.

BUSINESSMAN 1 and 2: Oil!

BUSINESSMAN 3: There must be something hidden under all that ice!

BUSINESSMAN 1 and 2: Yes!

BUSINESSMAN 1: Now, what else can we do to make life more pleasurable?

(*The* BUSINESSMEN *seriously examine the globe. Re-enter* CHILDREN OF THE RAINBOW.)

RED: How can you buy or sell the sky, the warmth of the land?

ORANGE: If we do not own the freshness of the air and the sparkle of the water, how can you buy or sell them?

YELLOW: Every part of this Earth is sacred. Every shining pine needle, every sandy shore, every mist in the dark woods. We are part of this Earth and it is part of us.

GREEN: The shining water that moves in the streams and rivers and oceans is not just water. It is the blood of our ancestors.

BLUE: There are strangers that come in the night and take from the land whatever they need. More than they need.

INDIGO: The Earth is not his brother, but his enemy and when he has conquered it, he moves on. His appetite will devour the Earth and leave behind only a desert.

VIOLET: He kidnaps the Earth from his children and he does not care.

(The BUSINESSMEN *are busily puffing on their cigars.)*

BUSINESSMAN 1: Industries, making this and making that.

BUSINESSMAN 2: Taking this and taking that.

BUSINESSMAN 3: Breaking this and breaking that.

BUSINESSMAN 1: Money in the bank, gold in the vault.

BUSINESSMAN 2: A little pollution, it's not our fault.

BUSINESSMAN 3: We'll fix it up later, a pinch of salt!

BUSINESSMAN 1: A little bit here and a little bit there.

BUSINESSMAN 2: Crushing the round and making it square.

BUSINESSMAN 3: Slush in the ponds and fug in the air.

ALL: What do we care!

(Satisfied, they laugh and shake hands. As the CHILDREN OF THE RAINBOW *come closer, the* BUSINESSMEN *look about them and keep themselves between the* CHILDREN *and the globe.)*

RED: The air is precious, for all things share the same breath.

ORANGE: The beast, the tree, the human, they all share the same breath.

YELLOW: The air shares its spirit with all the life it supports.

GREEN: All things are connected.

BLUE: Whatever befalls the Earth befalls the sons of the Earth.

INDIGO: The Earth does not belong to humans, humans belong to the Earth.

VIOLET: Man did not weave this web of life; he is merely a strand in it. Whatever he does to the web of life, he does to himself.

BUSINESSMAN 1: Why don't you run along and play.

RED: We are the children of the rainbow.

BUSINESSMAN 2: Colourful bunch, aren't they?

BUSINESSMAN 3: What do you know about the world, you're only children!

ORANGE: We are the spirit of the world.
BUSINESSMAN 1: (*Gets close to the Earth as if he would take it*) Spirit my foot, you're a bunch of rainbow loonies!
GREEN: Don't touch!
BLUE: Hands off!
BUSINESSMAN 2: Want your ball back, do you?
BUSINESSMAN 3: Well you can't have it.
BUSINESSMAN 1: It's ours!
(*They unfasten the strings holding the Earth.*)
CHILDREN: (*Together*) No!
INDIGO: Don't!
VIOLET: Please!
(*The* BUSINESSMEN *laugh and throw the ball to each other, over the heads of the* CHILDREN, *who try to stop them.*)
BUSINESSMAN 1: (*Holding ball and pounding it*) Take that! (*Laughing, throws it to* BUSINESSMAN 2.)
BUSINESSMAN 2: And that! (*Throws it to* BUSINESSMAN 3.)
(*The* BUSINESSMEN *throw the ball to each other, laughing and taunting. Eventually the* CHILDREN, *realizing they cannot retrieve the globe, begin to cry.*)
BUSINESSMAN 3: It's only a game!
RED: (*Aloud*) It isn't a game!
(*Thunder and lightning. High up above the highest rostrum, a glow, of all the colours of the rainbow appears. The* CHILDREN *assemble into a rainbow using the rostra to achieve the effect. Undaunted, the* BUSINESSMEN *now use the globe as a football. The* WARRIOR OF THE RAINBOW *appears at the top of the rostra.*)
WARRIOR: Stop! Stop! Stop, I say.
(*The* BUSINESSMEN *stop kicking the globe about.*)
BUSINESSMAN 1: Who the hell are you?
WARRIOR: I am the Warrior of the Rainbow, protector of the Earth. And these are my children.
BUSINESSMAN 2: Oh, is that so!
BUSINESSMAN 3: Well, fancy that!
WARRIOR: You miserable pathetic creatures! You greedy

selfish things! The Earth is precious and to harm the Earth is to heap contempt on its Creator!

BUSINESSMAN 1: What's he talking about?

BUSINESSMAN 2: It's been going on for years.

BUSINESSMAN 3: You can't blame us for everything.

WARRIOR: Listen to me! It is you who perpetuate the atrocities against the natural world because you are blinded by selfish greed and materiality. You are the vile cancer that clouds the sacred spirit, spreading pollution and destruction. Contaminate your bed and you will one night suffocate in your own waste. But in your perishing you will shine brightly, fired by the strength of the Creator. Look what you have done to the Earth!

(*The* BUSINESSMEN *look at the globe.*)

BUSINESSMAN 1: It's still roundish!

WARRIOR: Roundish! Roundish! Look at the havoc you have caused. Closer, look closer. Open your eyes!

BUSINESSMAN 2: There's a hole!

BUSINESSMAN 1: Where?

BUSINESSMAN 3: Here!

BUSINESSMAN 2: You did that!

BUSINESSMAN 3: Yeah, you were bashing it!

BUSINESSMAN 1: Well, it's not a very big hole. I didn't mean to do it! We'll stick a plaster on it!

BUSINESSMAN 3: That won't do any good!

BUSINESSMAN 2: It's growing!

BUSINESSMAN 1: What does that mean?

WARRIOR: Look closer!

BUSINESSMAN 2: It's dirty!

BUSINESSMAN 1: Dirty!

BUSINESSMAN 2: It's not new any more.

BUSINESSMAN 3: It's sticky. Sticky and dirty.

BUSINESSMAN 1: Tacky!

BUSINESSMAN 2: That's our home. You're talking about our home!

BUSINESSMAN 1: Well I didn't know it was this bad!

(BUSINESSMEN *examine the globe. The* CHILDREN *move forward.*)

WARRIOR: The children of the rainbow see all things.

RED: Air pollution.

ORANGE: Water pollution.

YELLOW: Soil pollution.

GREEN: Land degradation.

BLUE: Deforestation.

INDIGO: Species destruction.

VIOLET: Overpopulation.

RED: Ozone hole.

ORANGE: Greenhouse gases.

YELLOW: Overfished oceans.

GREEN: Nuclear threat.

BLUE: Acid rain.

INDIGO: Greed and pain.

VIOLET: Waste and more waste.

CHILDREN: (*Together*) Waste, waste. Waste and more waste.

BUSINESSMAN 1: But what can we do about it?

BUSINESSMAN 2 and 3: Yes, what can we do?

WARRIOR: Yes, what can we do?

WARRIOR: Listen to the spirit of the world. Think Earth first. You must feel for the Earth as if it were your own body. Think Earth first. Let your souls be touched by the spirit of the Earth.

(*The* CHILDREN OF THE RAINBOW *gather round and touch the* BUSINESSMEN.)

BUSINESSMAN 1: I feel strange.

BUSINESSMAN 2: So do I.

BUSINESSMAN 3: Me too.

BUSINESSMAN 1: Something's happening!

BUSINESSMAN 2: I feel . . . different.

BUSINESSMAN 3: I feel . . . I feel . . . odd!

WARRIOR: Feel for the Earth.

CHILDREN: (*Together*) Feel!

BUSINESSMAN 1: We must restore the forests.

BUSINESSMAN 2: Plant trees, many trees.
BUSINESSMAN 3: Forests are the lungs of the Earth.
CHILDREN: (*Together*) Feel!
BUSINESSMAN 2: We must protect all living species.
BUSINESSMAN 3: Stop wall of death fishing.
BUSINESSMAN 1: Share the Earth with all living things.
CHILDREN: (*Together*) Feel!

(*The* WARRIOR OF THE RAINBOW *exits unnoticed.*)

BUSINESSMAN 3: Utilize solar energy!
BUSINESSMAN 1: Retreat and recycle wastes.
BUSINESSMAN 2: Ban CFCs.
BUSINESSMAN 3: Protect Antarctica!
BUSINESSMAN 1: Promote environmentally friendly products.
BUSINESSMAN 2: Phase out nuclear weapons.
BUSINESSMAN 3: We must think Earth first!
BUSINESSMAN 2: Yes, Earth first!
BUSINESSMAN 1: Earth first!

(*They turn towards the* WARRIOR OF THE RAINBOW *but he has gone. The* CHILDREN *step back from the* BUSINESSMEN.)

BUSINESSMAN 2: He's gone!
BUSINESSMAN 3: Not entirely. Can't you feel him. Can't you feel his presence!
BUSINESSMAN 1: Yes!
BUSINESSMAN 2: You mean . . .
BUSINESSMAN 3: He's always amongst us!
BUSINESSMAN 1: (*Handing over the globe to* GREEN) Here, you'd better look after this. We've got work to do.
BUSINESSMAN 2: A lot of work.
BUSINESSMAN 3: Indeed!
BUSINESSMAN 1: We've got to put the Earth first. We've got plans to make, stratagems, designs for a greener world, for a more spiritual, environmentally enlightened world. Haven't we, boys?
BUSINESSMAN 2 and 3: You bet we have!
BUSINESSMAN 1: (*Exiting with* BUSINESSMAN 2 *and* 3) Right,

let's to it, then. We'll go straight to my office, call in all the heads of department and have a brainstorming session. Think Earth first!

(CHILDREN *delightedly polish up the globe and replace it in the original suspended state. Music 'Sing a Rainbow' (Arthur Hamilton). The* CHILDREN *sing.*

Sing a Rainbow

> Red and yellow and pink and green,
> Orange and purple and blue.
> I can sing a rainbow,
> Sing a rainbow, sing a rainbow too.
>
> Listen with your eyes,
> Please listen with your eyes,
> And sing everything you see.
> You can sing a rainbow,
> Sing a rainbow, sing along with me.

(*Repeat 'Red and yellow . . .'*)

(*Enter* WARRIOR OF THE RAINBOW, *who is now dressed in normal clothes as a balloon seller. In his hands he has seven strings attached to seven balloons, each one a different colour of the rainbow. They float in the air. He joins the* CHILDREN *in the song and hands each of them the balloon of their colouring. Balloons could have, 'Earth First' on them. Audience could be invited to join in the song.* CHILDREN *release their balloons into the audience. Enter* BUSINESSMEN, *each with bunch of balloons. They release them into the audience. All exit. Lights change to lingering spot on suspended Earth. Curtain.*)

THE END

HIGHLY COMMENDED: 15 AND OVER

GREENHEART AND THE DRAGON POLLUTANT

by Cressida Miles

EALING, LONDON,
ENGLAND

Characters

STORYTELLER
GREENHEART, the hero
THE DRAGON POLLUTANT
TWO DOCTORS
A FRIEND
NOAH
EVERYPERSON
ASSORTED ITEMS OF RUBBISH
(as many extras as available disguised
as different forms of pollution)

At the start of the play, the stage is gloomy, and littered with various bits of rubbish (waste paper and cans).

Enter STORYTELLER, *carrying placards.*

STORYTELLER:

We've come here this dark winter to brighten your day
With our tale which is based on an old mummer's play.
We've a hero called Greenheart, and he has a concern:
That the world to its proper state should return.
Our dragon, Pollutant, holds the earth in its power.
And in this dull time of year, finds the happiest hour.
There are a couple of battles, and in the end some good sense,
Now in just a few minutes the play will commence.
Please cheer for our Greenheart . . .
(*Holds up* *Hooray!* *placard.*)
No – louder . . . *Hooray!*
. . . and for the dragon shout Boo!
(*Holds up* **BOO!** *placard.*)
Then . . . (*Holds up* **BOO!** *and cups his ear.*)
Your help and goodwill could make our simple story true.
(*Enter* GREENHEART *with a broom.*)

GREENHEART:

In come I, your hero Greenheart.
Right here in this space is where I would start
To tidy up our world, and brighten the scene,
Which the Dragon Pollutant has made so unclean.
Like Hercules in the stables, I will undertake
To scrub out our environment for everyone's sake.
(*Starts to sweep and chant.*)
Packets and papers, tin cans and dust,
And disgusting old dinners, but clear it I must.

(GREENHEART *sweeps, tut-tutting sadly, but gets slower and slower.*)

STOREYTELLER:

Well Greenheart is at work, and doing his best.
(GREENHEART *sits down at one side.*)
He seems already tired and is taking some rest.
I fear he'll need more than his green-handled broom,
For the Dragon is threatening us with a devastating doom.
(STORYTELLER *stands to the side.*
Footsteps and sound of tin cans and broken bottles are heard offstage, followed by the DRAGON*'s rumbling and chuckling. Enter the* DRAGON.)

DRAGON: In come I, the dragon bold . . .

STORYTELLER: **BOO!**

DRAGON:

I've been around some time, but I'm not very old!
In fact I get younger every day,
Feeding on waste products you've all tossed away.
Pollutant they wrote on my last year's report,
But you lot can call me Poll for short.
I revel in factories emitting smoke.
Radioactive waste doesn't make me choke.
Give me a washing powder that won't biodegrade,
And acid rain by the bucketful for my lemonade!
Ah! . . .
(*Sighs with pleasure, but then starts sniffing around suspiciously.*)
Fee, Fi, Fo, Fum,
I smell the work of a green finger and thumb.
There's a new plant here, and the floor's swept clear.
Who are you? Where? Come out and stand here!
(GREENHEART *moves out of shadows, wearing a filter mask such as cyclists use against fumes, and carrying a waste-paper basket.*)
Ha! – an Environment Cleaner. Let him dare!

I've made this wicked hole in the ozone layer;
Nobody yet knows what that's going to do,
But something nasty is sure to come through.
This greenhearted creature shan't hinder my plan:
I'll smother him with rubbish as fast as I can.
(DRAGON *whistles to summon his retinue of rubbish – which can either be children dressed up as polluting rubbish, or a pile of boxes with appropriate labels brought in by a stage hand. The* DRAGON *proceeds to pile all this rubbish on to* GREENHEART, *who falls.*
STORYTELLER *holds up* **Aaah!** *placard.*)
Down goes old Greenheart, he wasn't much trouble.
Now we'll have a wonderful mucky world full of muddle.
I'll do what I like, and I'll live how I please;
You can all come and join me. I don't charge any fees.
(*The* DRAGON *goes off, smoking and kicking paper about. Enter* DOCTORS *with small torches.*)

DOCTOR 1: I'm Dr Keep Britain Tidy.

STORYTELLER: *Hooray!*

DOCTOR 2: I'm Dr Lead Free.

STORYTELLER: *Hooray!*

DOCTOR 1: We're on the same side as Greenheart, you see.

DOCTOR 2: With a little light on the scene, we shall soon set all right,

DOCTOR 1: And Greenheart will rise up to go out and fight.
(*They revive* GREENHEART, *who shakes hands with them, and goes to sit down in a corner. Exit* DOCTORS.)

GREENHEART:
Ah, poor old world! What hope can I bring!
We've all the despair of winter without the promise of spring!
The dragon is evil, but he has the best tune.
To his powers of persuasion we are none of us immune.
(*Puts his head in his hands in despair.*
Enter FRIEND.)

FRIEND:

In come I, Greenheart's Friend, in his hour of need.

STORYTELLER: *Hooray!*

I have something in this book, which I thought I would read.

(*Holds up a green-covered book called* Queeries and Dancers.)

Are you concerned that we treat our God's earth
With enlightened respect and a sense of its worth?

GREENHEART:

Yes of course I'm concerned, but it's all been no good.
I've tried to resist just as hard as I could.
But I see that this monster is much greater than me:
Its greenhouse effect is even moving the sea!
Our civilization will be buried in layers of mud,
And we shall be drowned in a terrible flood.

(*Enter* NOAH.)

NOAH:

Did I hear someone say flood in here?
I, Mr Noah, tell you all not to fear.
I know all about wetting the world, by golly.
I had to save animals from humankind's folly.
We've had a flood before, and it turned out alright:
God sent us a rainbow, a promising light.

FRIEND:

Light is the answer, a light from inside.
We need every person's light on our side.

(*Enter* EVERYPERSON.)

EVERYPERSON:

In come I, Everyperson.
Now, what's on your minds, I'm ready to listen.

GREENHEART:

Are you concerned about pollution?

(EVERYPERSON *nods.*)

We think we may have found a solution,
But we need your help against old Polly,

And your light to brighten this darkness and folly.

FRIEND:

Call out the doctors, Keep Britain Tidy and Lead Free.
The more we are enlightened the better, you'll see.
(STORYTELLER *steps forward.*)

STORYTELLER:

I think that these fellows have a worthwhile plan.
How will Poll fight this one? Let's see if it can.

(GREENHEART, FRIEND, EVERYPERSON *and the* DOCTORS *arm themselves with dustbin bags, torches and lanterns. They also bring on a vacuum cleaner. The stage becomes lighter.*

The dragon's footsteps (and sound of tin cans and broken bottles) are heard offstage. Enter the DRAGON *with a few only of his retinue. He is grumbling and groaning.*)

STORYTELLER: **BOO!**

DRAGON: (*In injured tones . . .*)

But I'm old Poll the dragon, you all know me!

STORYTELLER: **BOO!**

DRAGON:

I use what I need and throw the rest in the sea,
But just lately I've seen people scooping it out.
I can't think what all the fuss is about.
We've always had litter, so now what's new?
These ecology conscious people are getting you all in a stew.
It's really not fair to take on in this way!
I'm willing to compromise, so let's call it a day!

GREENHEART:

It is a day, Poll my friend, but it's our new day too.
We are lighting the way on a path that is true.
(*All shine their lights on the* DRAGON *who tries to get away from the glare by lying down.*)

DRAGON:

Now this green fellow's got under my skin.
I daren't open my eyes because light's getting in!

(*While the dragon is down,* GREENHEART, FRIEND,

EVERYPERSON *and the* DOCTORS *scoop up rubbish into their dustbin bags, and bundle it offstage.*)

GREENHEART:

Now we'll recycle this rubbish in any way that we can.
To use, not to waste is all part of our plan.
(DOCTORS *bring out a 'save the world' banner and hang it round the* DRAGON*'s neck.* EVERYPERSON *helps the* DRAGON *up, and demonstrates the vacuum cleaner.*

EVERYPERSON:

Yes, you and I, Dragon, will have to be taught
How to use our resources in the way that we ought.
We must look to the state of the world that we leave,
And see that it's safe for our children to breathe.
Come on Poll, mend your ways, you can't always be winning.
It won't be that easy, but it's a new beginning.
(STORYTELLER *holds up* [*Hooray!*] *placard. They lead the drooping* DRAGON *off, trailing the vacuum cleaner, to the tune of the wassailing song, with drumbeat. Only* STORYTELLER *is left onstage.*)

STORYTELLER:

Inside my friend Greenheart and inside you and me,
There's a light that revives us and sets us all free.
To work all together for a cause that is right
Is one way to harness the power that might
Bring goodness and mercy, and light up a star,
Like the Christmas one long ago, so near and so far
We hope you've enjoyed our tale and its end,
And good wishes to you in the New Year we all send!

Now come on in, Greenheart, and here take a bow,
[*Hooray!*] [**CLAP** (Loudly!)]
And you too, Dragon Poll:
[*Hooray!*] [**CLAP** (Loudly!)]

And Everyperson now,
Hooray! CLAP (Loudly!)

With our Friend, and Noah,
Hooray! CLAP (Loudly!)

and the doctors two,
Hooray! CLAP (Loudly!)

Not forgetting myself –
Hooray! CLAP (Loudly!)

this is all of our crew!
We hope you've enjoyed our tale, and its end
And good wishes to you in the New Year we send.

ALL (*Singing*):
We've played a little tale about a dragon that we found
And how he threatened Nature, throwing rubbish all around.
Your papers and your empty cans, give us if you please,
Aye and give us back a new world, where we can safely breathe.

Here we come a-wassailing, among the leaves so green.
Here we come a-wandering, so fairly to be seen.
Now is winter time, but spring will soon be here,
And we wish you and send you a happy new year.

STORYTELLER: Hooray! CLAP (Loudly!)

THE END

HIGHLY COMMENDED: 15 AND OVER

THINK GLOBAL, ACT LOCO

A play in one act

by Rick Whisenand

BANGKOK, THAILAND

AUTHOR'S NOTE

This play is based on stories about Eskimo shamans from the book *Teachings from the American Earth* by Tedlock and Tedlock (Liveright, New York, 1975). When the Eskimo run short of game or the weather is foul, a shaman is asked to travel beneath the earth to attend to the sea spirit Takanakapsaluk, who is sick and dirty from people's abuse of her and from their other sins. When he returns, the villagers have to confess and promise to live better. Another influence comes from the books by Carlos Castaneda, mainly in the characters like Don Genaro and Castaneda himself.

There is a very difficult point in the play when the shaman actor, as Jones, also has to travel beneath the earth – he draws a circle on the stage and all the pain, fury and disgust the earth holds is conducted through him and comes out in a horrible cry. Older students, perhaps at university level, or teachers – people with some energy and imagination – might be able to pull it off.

The main thing to remember when acting Jones is that he considers his behaviour 'controlled folly', except when dealing with the earth. As for Dada and Gaga, they think that what they are doing is important and real, so they self-inflate easily but are easily punctured, too. They believe in themselves, even though in essence they have no real existence; the actors don't need to worry about characterization or getting into the part – they simply have to do it, and all the audience has to believe is that they are indeed doing it (that is, the actors need to 'project'.)

Jones, on the other hand, has no self to believe in, having tried to wipe any 'self' out of existence, to make himself 'formless', so that he can act with complete abandon and complete control. The actor's job is to make as much out of it as he can, to block and shock the others and treat them like straw dogs. If he has the same effect on the audience, so much the better.

Finally, the characters talk about being on a floor rather than the ground, because they probably will be. The pain of lumber is the earth's pain too.

Characters

JONES
DADA
GAGA

Lights on only over the audience; the only light on stage is that from the house, so the action can take place downstage or on the apron. Curtain opens on to a bare stage. No light cue for audience. After a spell, a man, JONES, *walks on from the shadows upstage, carrying an old acoustic guitar; he doesn't wait for the audience to quieten, pays them no mind. He sits cross-legged, down right, guitar beside him; he makes himself comfortable and casually adopts the Buddha attitude of 'calling the Earth to witness', left hand in lap, right hand on knee or calf, fingers touching the ground – so casual is he, is fact, that the casual observer wouldn't think of it as a meditation pose. He keeps his eyes open, looking from one place to another, including the audience. After awhile, he takes up his guitar and plays an accompaniment to what he sees – not a tune, just sounds and percussion, perhaps singing like a gipsy or a rough Dylan. It's important that he never be 'lost in the music' or 'deep into himself'; what goes into his eyes and passes through him from the ground comes out of his fingers and mouth, which makes it an exercise in* not-doing. *I hope it will have spirit, but anything consciously soulful is a slip of attention.*

After about a minute of this, DADA *and* GAGA *enter from the wings, left, and move toward* JONES, *but not wishing to disturb him they keep their distance. He seems not to notice them, but his music has new sounds, responding to them. They politely wait for him to finish, but eventually realize that, as he's playing no known tune, he probably won't finish, so* DADA *opens.*

DADA: Excuse me.

(JONES *answers with his guitar, pauses, gently strums one more time, and turns to them. His manner instantly changes.*)

JONES: (*Shrieks like a woman*) Whaddaya want!! (*Hold, then laugh.*)

GAGA: Nothing, thanks!

(*Starts off. To* DADA) Let's go.

DADA: (*Ignores him*) Excuse me, we're looking for a man by the name of –

JONES: Wait, let me guess! (*Stands and thinks very hard.*) Oh, yeah! He's not here, go away.

DADA: (*Unfazed, tries to get around this subterfuge*) A friend of yours said that you could help us.

(JONES *slips his guitar over his shoulder and starts moving around the stage, as if he's stalking prey or looking for a good position to ambush them from. He keeps on the move, sometimes close, sometimes far.*)

GAGA: I don't think he wants to see us, if it *is* him.

DADA: Your friend was quite positive about how much you knew concerning the state of the natural world and thought you would have a lot to tell us we might find useful in our work.

GAGA: This 'friend of yours' line has never worked . . . Besides, he's out of it, as you can see, and I don't want to talk to him anyway, so let's go.

DADA: (*Light and easy*) You know, we've come a long way to see you, we wonder if you might, you know, let us join you for a spell at least, and maybe just sit and talk a bit . . . We're from an organization that's dedicated to doing volunteer work for the environment. And our group is also interested – at least, our special interest sub-group is – in investigations of the more spiritual or psychological –

JONES: (*Shouts*): Environment?!

DADA: Pardon?

JONES: (*Whispers*) Environment?

GAGA: What?

JONES: Ah-ha!

(*He mimes slamming a door.*) SLAM. (*And turns his back to them.*)

DADA: (*To* GAGA) I was going to say something.

GAGA: And I ruined it all. Yeah, and it's my fault we're dealing with a psycho-schizo medicine man.

DADA: He's a *shaman* – there's a big difference, as you know, and it *is* your fault.

GAGA: Shaman shmaman, all I –

JONES: (*Pokes his head around the 'door'*) Who says there ain't no rhyme for oranges?
(*Goes back in.*) SLAM.

GAGA: (*Yells through the door*) I say!
(JONES *cackles loudly and gleefully, stops suddenly.*)

GAGA: (*Under* DADA*'s disapproving look*) OK, OK, I'm sorry, I'll stop antagonizing your precious loony holy man. He's all yours.

DADA: I think there's a method to his madness, that's what it is.
(*He takes* GAGA *aside and downstage.*)
This is the rite of passage, the initiation, the trial by fire, the test of our worthiness to receive the secret knowledge. We're on a kind of vision quest – your words, remember?

GAGA: Well, it's not all it was cracked up to be.

DADA: That doesn't matter. We've come all this way to find our golden fleece, our holy grail, maybe even the meaning of it all, who knows? All we need to do is gain his trust and prove we're the right –
(*Meanwhile,* JONES *has turned and is leaning on his guitar as if it were a broadsword; he takes a few practice swings with it, then lifts it high, bellows, and charges. They scatter. The Trials ensue, which can be worked out in rehearsal; some are physical, some verbal, mainly intended to shock* DADA *and* GAGA *and keep them off balance.*
At the end of The Trials, JONES *and the two are on opposite sides of the stage. He takes an imaginary coin from his pocket and holds it out to them.*)

JONES: Here is a dime. Call your mother and tell her you'll never save the earth.

GAGA: (*Pause; low*) It costs a quarter.

JONES: That is the only intelligent thing you –

DADA: (*Righteously insulted*) You can't treat us like this. We came here in good faith to learn from you, and you haven't done anything but insult us and try to drive us as crazy as you are!

JONES: Don't tell me you're mad at last!

GAGA: Let's get the hell *out* of here!

DADA: Yeah we're mad, real fed up, *real* mad!

JONES: So let's hear it! Show me what you're gonna do to me! Lemme hear what you got! Tear me up, yea team go!

GAGA: Damnit, would you shut up!!

JONES: That's the spirit!

(*A bit of* ad lib *here, up to a pathetic kind of climax on the part of* DADA *and* GAGA.)

Oh, *wow*.

(*Pause*.)

Who are you mad at, your grandmother?

(*He moves in a little*.)

Here I am. Come and get me.

(*He takes a wrestler crouch*.

DADA *and* GAGA *are not really in the mood; self-consciously they start to circle him in opposite directions*. JONES *carefully keeps them in sight as they close in, and then leaps on to* DADA *and pins him to the ground in a trice*. DADA *struggles and yelps until he is let up*. GAGA *hesitates, tries to pull* JONES *off, but he can't*.)

JONES: (*To* GAGA) Count one two three! . . . C'mon, count one two three.

GAGA: (*Sits back*) One two three.

JONES: No, you've got to slap the mat; now, once more with feeling!

GAGA: (*Once more, without much feeling*) One, Two, Three.

(JONES *bounds up and stands back, stretches himself*. GAGA *is sitting morosely on the ground, and* DADA *eventually pulls himself upright*. *Silence*.)

DADA: I just can't figure out why you're doing this to us. (*No answer*.) We haven't done anything to you, we just wanted to talk to you. (*No answer.*) We didn't mean to insult you, nothing personal, no harm intended. We only wanted to find out something about . . . (*gestures*) all this, the world.

JONES: (*Pause*) I'm not insulted. I'm not hurt . . . But maybe I can find someone who is.

(*He walks around them, surveying everything, and comes back to his place. Then he sits as at the beginning. After awhile he leans forward, kneels, and traces with his hand a circle on the floor. As he does so, a scream builds inside him and he erupts, retching with fury and agony, sweating blood.*
When the fit passes, he sits with his knees drawn up to his chest, breathing deeply and slowly; then he gets up and stretches all over. DADA *is struck with awe.* GAGA *is not sure what he saw.* JONES *sits back down and faces them. Long silence.*)

DADA: (*Low*) Are we going to try?

(*Silence.*)

GAGA: You probably expect me to do that.

(*Silence.*)

DADA: What did you do?

GAGA: What's going on?

DADA: You just . . . ?

GAGA: It's just a circle on the floor.

DADA: Where did that . . . sound . . . ?

GAGA: You call that doing something?

DADA: Did you really . . . ?

GAGA: Is that supposed to help?

DADA: Does it help?

GAGA: What the hell good does that do?

DADA: I want to know . . . how . . .

GAGA: I can't even remember why we're here.

DADA: Can you tell me . . . ?

GAGA: I wish I could remember how to get back to the highway.

DADA: (*Pause*) Could you show us again?

GAGA: I didn't see anything.

(*Silence.*)

DADA: (*bends over*) It's our turn to touch the earth. I want to feel what the earth feels. I want to know what the earth knows.

(*He slowly reaches forwards.* JONES *quietly shifts into kneeling position.* GAGA *inches away in the other direction, an eye on* DADA.)

If we could do that, we would understand everything, we would become pure and whole again, we would find the true meaning of paradise, on this earth.

(*His hand trembles as it gets nearer. Just before it touches the floor,* JONES *goes into convulsions of laughter, rolling on the floor.*)

JONES: (*Falsetto*) Ow! Stop! Stop it! You're tickling me! Quit it, I say!

(*He goes on a bit after* DADA *quits and sits, disgusted, the spell broken.* JONES *pretends to realize that no one thinks he's funny, then sits up and acts as if it were someone else. Silence.* DADA *stares hard at him pulling his innocent act. He gets up and speaks to* GAGA.)

DADA: I'm sick of these games. Let's go.

(GAGA *gets up and they start off.* JONES *stands too.*)

JONES: Hey, hold on a sec!

(*They turn.*)

Was it something I said?

DADA: (*After a pause, in which he girds up his girdle*) Do you mind if I have a few words with you?

(*Approaches.*)

JONES: Yeah, you tell 'im, bro! (*To* GAGA) Come on, that's your line, 'Yeah, you tell 'im, bro!'

GAGA: I'm going to go have a cigarette.

(*He doesn't move.* JONES *looks at him and then howls with glee again, real tears, the works.*)

JONES: (*Drying his eyes, arm around* DADA) But hey, no offence, really, why don't you try again, here you go.

(*Sets him down by the circle, opens an imaginary lid, and shouts down.*)
Hey, Ma! There's some guys up here wanna talk to you!
(*Listens.*)
I don't know! Something about . . . uhh . . . well, I don't know – here, I'll ask him!
(*To* DADA) She wants to know what you want to see her about.

GAGA: Are you trying to prove something with this crap?

JONES: (*Absently*) Yeah.
(*To* DADA) Mebbe it'd be better if you talked to her yourself. Here. Oh, and (*leans in*) just between you and me, you ain't gonna get to first base with that other kinda talk, y'know what I mean; try being a little more . . . natural-like. A little sincerity goes a long way with a lady. OK.
(*He sits back, gives the floor to* DADA. DADA *leans over a little, doesn't know what to say.*)

DADA: My friend and I . . . We want to help you . . . you see . . .

JONES: Excuse me, but I think it could use a bit more . . . conviction.

DADA: I feel ridiculous.

JONES: It's too ordinary for words, isn't it?
(*He laughs and gets his guitar, returns. During most of what remains, he quietly plays an accompaniment, notes that seem random.*)

DADA: (*Again to the floor*) We came here because . . . we want to do something to protect you. We belong to an organization dedicated to saving the environment and –
(*A loud twang from* JONES *interrupts him.*)

JONES: Now what did I say about language?

DADA: I don't know what to say to a floor!
(*Pause.* JONES *looks at* GAGA, *and so does* DADA.) Could you try? I mean, this was all your idea, anyway.

GAGA: OK.

(He and DADA *trade places.* GAGA *had been showing interest, so he has lost most of his petulance; he has found something to take seriously. He speaks clearly and naturally to the floor, but doesn't bend over.)*

GAGA: We thought this would be easy. We thought we could just come out here and 'sit at the feet of the master' while he filled us with beautiful stories about how precious you are and how we could save you. We were, or *I* was, hoping to put it in a book or a video or something. (*Pause.*) *Have* I hurt you and insulted you? (*Pause.*) I still don't know exactly how. (*Silence.*) The easy road, the routine . . . blaming everyone else, looking to someone else. Yeah, I've done that before. And now . . . (*Silence.*) I can't believe all the things I believed before, but I'll probably keep doing the same things . . . If I can talk to you sometimes, and remember that you *are* here, that would help . . . I know it would help me, but what can I do about other people? That's the main reason I'm doing this. No one pays any attention and they go off on their same old ways and you get worse and worse. Do they *want* to know? (*Silence.* JONES *also silent.*) They just don't want to be told. We want to know, but we don't want to be told. (*Long silence. Guitar resumes.*) It's been nice talking to you. Thanks for your help. Maybe we'll get to talk again sometime.
(*To* DADA.) Say, goodbye to her.

DADA: (*Comes over, still not sure*) Goodbye. Thank you.
(GAGA *stands, and* JONES. *They shake hands.*)

GAGA: Thank you. I'm not really sure what happened today, but I'll think about it, and maybe something will come out of it.

DADA: If we were to come by again, say, next weekend, would you be available?

JONES: Would I need to be?

DADA: (*Pause*) I can't understand what we can do if people don't want to be told. It doesn't make sense.

GAGA: (*Starts off*) That's what makes it interesting.
DADA: (*Also going*) But what are we supposed to *do*?
GAGA: We could always try *not-doing*.
DADA: *Not-doing*. I don't think the committee's going to be too thrilled about *not-doing*.

(GAGA *laughs and they exit into the wings.* JONES *starts up his guitar and singing, and he goes back into the darkness upstage. Curtain.*)

THE END

HIGHLY COMMENDED: 15 AND OVER

PERSEPHONE AND THE RUBBISH BIN

by St Peter's Youth Group

KIRKCALDY, FIFE, SCOTLAND

Characters

DEMETER, earth goddess
PERSEPHONE, daughter of Demeter
PI, a young boy
MAID
HADES
BLACK PROTAGONIST
WHITE PROTAGONIST
CROWD OF SIX PEOPLE
READER

Scene 1

Characters: Demeter, Persephone, Pi, Maid, Hades
Props: well, globe, flowers, stool, shepherd's crook, flute

The stage is covered with flowers. There is an ancient well in the centre. DEMETER, *mother of* PERSEPHONE, *sits downstage left of the well, watching while her daughter, her* MAID *and* PI *sit/lie downstage right decorating a globe of the world with flowers.* PI *plays a flute.*

DEMETER:

My daughter is happy,
The world grows abundant,
Life swells in the grape,
Elves dance in attendance
No pillage, no violence, or even rape.
The heads of corn bend down with a will,
Delivering the seed that in some future will bring
Visions to young men, patterns to fulfil,
In the weaving wonder of an ecstatic spring.
Yet something now creeps deep and low
Around my heart and within my song.
It's the noble tree supports the silent mistletoe,
I fear a great truth hidden in a great wrong.
Over which golden head will this dark destiny break?
I, the mother of my daughter wish it were me
That my body be pierced for my daughter's sake,
As the great Earth suffers its child of humanity.
But now Persephone speaks.
(PERSEPHONE *moves towards well, carrying decorated globe,* MAID *follows.*)

PERSEPHONE:

Mother of mothers, I dance in your day,
So bright and full green and gay.

Young Pi has blown a full strange song,
Even now my ears quiver and my head does throng
With its call of love
Plunging towards a hideous fate.
Mother?

DEMETER: Pi!

PI: (*Moves to centre front*) Separate!

MAID:

What can he mean,
This boy of seven?
Who is he? Whose son has he been,
This boy of seven
Whose face is so keen?
Ah! Mistress pay little heed,
For your head not your heart
Provides for all you need.
We women know well what can start
Once we lay claim
To the mysterious arts.

PERSEPHONE: Maid! Be quiet, you've never been in love.

MAID: Seeing not believing has always been my stuff!

PERSEPHONE:

You are coarse and rude,
You chase my dreams away.
You are bold in our words
But you would not move
To look down this well
And cast a whisper to play
Down its vaulted depths
Not tomorrow nor now – today!

MAID: Not even in jest, Persephone!

PI: Perhaps even in truth, Persephone.

DEMETER: Nor even I, Persephone.

(*Enter* HADES, *back left*.)

HADES:

And even *now*, Persephone,

I am not complete
(*Crossing to* PERSEPHONE *at the well.*)
You will be mine
Your mother shall reap
All she has sown
Under this hot sun,
For I shall have Beauty,
She shall not have all,
Not with her daughter
To grace my underground Hall.
(PERSEPHONE *drops decorated globe into well as* HADES *lures her away.*)

PERSEPHONE:
Mother, I have known only you,
Yet a love calls for me to be true
To the dark and the feared, to a soul in pain.
Mother, goodbye – will I return again
Will I return?
(*Fading away.*) Again?

DEMETER: Daughter, Persephone . . .

Scene 2

Characters: Black protagonist, White protagonist, crowd of six people wearing half-white, half-black masks.
Props: Rubbish bin and rubbish; models of factory, prison, school, nuclear power station, bank, supermarket and church; globe; drill (optional).

The well has transformed into rubbish bin. A CROWD OF SIX *in half-white and half-black masks flank either side of the bin. In front of the bin are two protagonists; one (left) full* BLACK, *one full* WHITE. *They are scavenging from inside the bin, models of social institutions. During this scene they each claim three models which are then placed front stage in a row to make a city skyline. The seventh and final model is the Earth:*

BLACK: (*Takes out model of chemical factory.*)

Out of this smelly and polluted pit
I'm gonna make load a' money fast.
Who else to challenge it?
Lots a' muck and lots a' brass,
And look at this blackened mimicry,
A nice toxic chemical factory
Why would anyone throw this away?

WHITE:

Well, perhaps it was that it didn't pay.
However, with the right sort of advertising,
Market research,
Finance and executive in-fighting,
We'll make it work.
(*Takes factory.*)
So give it to me, and don't look so hurt!

CROWD: (*While model is placed*)

Is it yours? Is it his?
It will make no difference
To our families and kids.

WHITE: (*Takes out prison*)

Now this again is more my style,
A nice social institution,
10,000 prisoners to the mile.
Just right for redevelopment
An exercise in market forces.

BLACK:

I'd be a little careful with that my friend,
It contains my bombs, bombers, gunmen and arms,
Enough to sink all your dividends,
(*Snatches prison.*)
Despite your talk and after-shave smarm.
(*Places at front.*)

CROWD:

Oh dear, look at them play,

Divide the Earth,
Have a nice day!

BLACK: (*Takes out school*)
Ah, here's a school – come out to play!
I can teach you the things beyond your dreams,
Robocop Five and Turtles Six,
Just enough to make you shiver and scream,
Polluting your values and making you rich.

WHITE:
Bloodstained hands holding our schools,
What an offence and utter depravity,
You must think us all fools,
Not to protect a matter of such gravity.
No! We aim to give a sound education,
based securely on entrepreneurial vocation.
(WHITE *takes school*.)
No need to explore the world's foundation.
(*Places at front*.)

CROWD:
The children, the children, how they debase them,
Their right to the earth and not to their nation!

WHITE: (*Takes out nuclear power station*)
Oh yes. A nice little earner,
A nuclear power station complete with waste,
Masses of loans and interest in the future.
Never mind what it does and how it generates,
It's going to be here forever,
Fission – the final sweepstake.

BLACK:
By rights, the only power this possesses
Is a bomb for times of great stresses.
Yes, it's mine; I wouldn't use it wildly
Just a little insurance
(*Takes station*.)
To talk the nutter over quietly.
(*Places at front*.)

CROWD: What is Beauty, where has she gone?
Into the Earth – replaced by a bomb!
BLACK: (*Taking out bank*)
Ah! I could do a lot with a bank
Take all the cheques
Leaving them blank.
And what would I do next?
Well, I could buy the oil states.
WHITE:
You could never profit from an Arab sheikh,
You would just stuff money in a suitcase.
It takes a certain way with figures,
(*Taking bank.*)
A secret stolen there, a word dropped here,
And a subtle mixture of ordinary fear.
(*Places at front.*)
CROWD:
Push and shove, power and politics,
Always so boring, never any novelties.
WHITE: (*Taking out supermarket*)
Food is grown but prices are hard hit,
Milk from a bottle and peas a packet.
Ignorance is profitable in the supermarket,
It's centralized, chemicalized,
And I don't really want it!
BLACK:
Just give it to me,
There's power to be had,
From people's indigestion.
And though poisoning is sad,
(*Taking supermarket.*)
It meets my intention.
(*Places at front.*)
CROWD:
Man's relationship with the planet
Is being cut down the middle

Like a cake at a banquet.

BLACK: (*Taking out church*)

Now we all need a Church and I can deliver
A God in a package who puts friend to the front
And enemies to the rear,
A church which supports the traditional idea.

WHITE:

What blasphemy you blackened knave.
Give that to me,
And watch how you behave.
(*Taking church.*)
My church is more for making the people afraid
Of who they are – nice woolly sheep.
(*Places at front.*)

CROWD:

Is this the final outrage or is there worse to come?
We are supposed to be the children of God's Kingdom.

WHITE: (*Taking out globe*) What's this?

BLACK: It looks valuable.

CROWD: Aaaah!

WHITE: Careful, it may explode.

BLACK: I'm used to bombs – this one's too old.

WHITE: There's something inside . . .

BLACK: We will have to divide . . .

WHITE: Using technology and skill . . .

BLACK: (*Producing real/imaginary drill*) And a great big drill.

WHITE: Hold it quiet, hold it firm.

BLACK: Avert your eyes, this'll make you squirm.

(*They try to drill into the globe.*)

CROWD:

What monstrous things they do to our Earth,
Our Mother and standard of beauty.
Stop, stop, we will all be cursed,
Midgets consumed in a war of the mighty.

WHITE: I can make no impression!

BLACK: I've a headache coming on.

WHITE: I feel a little bit strange.
BLACK: The light begins to wane.
WHITE and BLACK:
Nothing here not for us,
Let's throw it away,
Ashes to ashes, dust to dust.
(*They toss the globe back into the bin and stand back, shaken.*)
CROWD: Hiss.

Scene 3

Characters: Pi, crowd of six, reader.
Props: Bin and rubbish, bucket, newspapers, walkman, drink cans, cigarettes.

The CROWD *is now fanning out from the bin, reading newspapers, drinking from cans, smoking, listening to walkmans, listless, dull.* PI *comes in with a bucket, seeking water from the crowd.*
CROWD MEMBER 1: *Turns away, absorbed in walkman music, not noticing* PI.
CROWD MEMBER 2: *Walks past* PI, *absorbed in newspaper.*
CROWD MEMBER 3: *Flicks ash into his bucket.*
CROWD MEMBER 4: *Tosses beer can into his bucket.*
CROWD MEMBER 5: *Brushes him away.*
CROWD MEMBER 6: *Examines inside of bucket then walks off.*
Eventually, PI *dips his water bucket hopefully in the rubbish bin. It is filled with rubbish when he brings it out. He attempts, even so, to drink it. Apparently poisoned he collapses to the floor. As these silent actions take place there is this reading.*
READER:
To lift your eyes to heaven
When all men's eyes are on the ground
Is not easy.
To worship at the feet of the angels
When all men worship only fame and riches,

Is not easy.
But the most difficult of all,
Is to think the thoughts of the angels,
To speak the words of the angels,
And to do as angels do.

In the days of old when the Creation was young,
The Earth was filled with giant trees,
Whose branches soared above the clouds,
And in them dwelled our ancient fathers,
They who walked with the angels
And who lived by the Holy Law.
Through their forests flowed the Eternal River
And in the centre stood the Tree of Life.
They ate from the table of the Earthly Mother
And slept in the arms of the Heavenly Father.
Now the desert sweeps the Earth with burning sand,
The giant trees are dust and ashes,
Now the path leading to the Tree of Life
Is hidden from the eyes of men
And sorrow fills the empty sky.

Scene 4

Characters: Crowd of six, Pi, Demeter, Black, White, Persephone, Hades.
Props: Well covered with lid and tablecloth, goblet.

The bin/well is transformed into a table. SIX MEMBERS OF THE CROWD, BLACK *and* WHITE *protagonists are 'sitting' at the table arguing about food and dinner.* PI *still lies centre front stage, apparently dead.*
MEMBER 1: I'm starving, I'm hungry. Who's cooking dinner?
MEMBER 2: Well, I'm not eating; I'm looking after my figure.
MEMBER 3: I couldn't find a burger so I got some chips.

MEMBER 4: You! You couldn't cook them, you haven't got the wits.

MEMBER 5: It wouldn't be so bad, but I've never been taught.

MEMBER 6: Even if you had, you wouldn't be the right sort, You don't know the difference between a carrot and a pea.

MEMBER 5: I do so! One's grown in an orchard, the other is fished from the sea.

MEMBER 3: What's all this about – we haven't any water –

MEMBER 4: And I'm starving.

MEMBER 2: And I'm thirsty.

(*Enter* DEMETER *in disguise.*)

DEMETER: Have you seen my daughter?

BLACK: Who's she?

WHITE: What's her name?

DEMETER: Her name? Persephone.

ALL:

That name is lost, beyond it we are mute.
We cannot recall,
It does not compute.
We found to our cost that modern learning is a burden
For any who enters
The garden of Eden.

DEMETER:

Oh children, my children, I have walked the Earth
For days and nights,
I see hunger and thirst,
All manner of confusion and petty blight.
For years upon years, weary in this cloak,
I have sought my daughter, child of the world,
Through fields of famine and petrifying snows,
Asking the people as each season unfurls
Where their beauty is hidden but nobody knows.
As a play inside a play, a dream within a dream,
Is man enrapt in his self-made world,
Blind to his own part in the overall scheme?

ALL:

Who are you that you talk to us
In manner so strange and mysterious?

DEMETER: (*Casting off cloak*)

What need now of this disguise?
I cast it off and show my magnificence.
Though now I am in pain, it will cause no surprise
To see my lost, my search become nonsense.
So here I am, my name is Demeter.
I come for my daughter
But you have not seen her.
(*Sees* PI.)
Yet here is one who lies so quiet.
What is his name – hear my cry!

ALL: He has always been there. His name is Pi.

DEMETER:

Now I quickly sense all that has been.
I hold my hands to his sleeping head,
My power of old to make men dream
Should his spirit be not yet dead.
Yes, he stirs,
He's moving around.
I will ask him my question.
Please not a sound.
Young Pi – my daughter,
Have you seen?

PI: (*Waking*)

My head swims, my eyes hardly see
I have had a great dream
A girl – lovely – beauty – Persephone.

DEMETER:

Almighty God, I thank you in heaven
For giving that name in the midst of sleep.
What magic there is in a child of seven,
Giving a secret that no man of seventy could keep.
Quickly young Pi – where is she hid?

PI:

It is unclear but there is something resembling a lid
(DEMETER *snatches the tablecloth off, revealing the old well.*)
Her time has come,
Her labour is finished,
The child is won
To man's soul undiminished.
She has the water
From beyond the grave
Her mother has sought her,
A marriage anulled,
A husband in black – a man of sorrows
Her love has fulfilled . . .
Now she comes
And he follows.

(*Enter* PERSEPHONE *and* HADES *from well. He holds a goblet.*)

PERSEPHONE: I return, my head is clear.
HADES: I love you greatly, I do fear.
PERSEPHONE: One thousand years.
HADES: And many tears.
PERSEPHONE: We have a child.
HADES: Beauty sublime.
PERSEPHONE: See the child is here.
HADES: (*Gives chalice to* PI) Drink this water – it is wine.
PERSEPHONE: Share it Pi with our Earth and sky.
With black and white though they know not why.
(*All share cup and shed black masks and tunics/gowns, now in multi colours.*)

ALL:

Feed our Earth and heed the whale,
Not just reason, but beauty prevail
Upon this world our mother's soft skin
Let us tread lightly to hear the angels sing.

THE END

Sacred Earth Drama Competition
Terms and Conditions

Our hope is to encourage people of all ages to become involved in environmental thinking and practice by first involving their creative spirit. We invite schools, theatre groups, community organizations and individuals to create new plays which are based on religious or mythical stories and say something about the natural world and how we should live in it. The plays should be as imaginative as possible, not too wordy, not too long. We are particularly keen for plays that can be performed by schools.

1. Entries should take the form of a play script. Photos, video or cassette recordings can be sent as supporting material but are not essential.
2. It is suggested that entries be 20–45 minutes long.
3. There are two age categories for judging: under 15, and 15 and over.
4. No entry fee is required and scripts will not be returned.
5. All entrants whose plays are selected for publication will receive a fee in lieu of book royalties and royalties for public performances outside of schools.
6. Entrants retain the copyright of their plays but assign the exclusive worldwide publishing licence to the Sacred Earth Drama Trust, should their plays be selected for publication within two years of submission. Rights for further development of the play by other media remain with the author.
7. Entries may be sent any time but the closing date for the annual judging is Earth Day, 22 April, each year.
8. Inquiries and requests for entry forms to: Sacred Earth Drama Trust, Kilnhurst, Kilnhurst Road, Todmorden, Lancashire OL14 6AX, Great Britain. Phone: (0706) 816 582; Fax: (0706) 816 359.

The Sacred Earth Drama Trust is a registered charity, no. 1000221.